FIREFIGHTER!

By the same author

Fireman! A Personal Account

Firemen at War

999 – The Accident and Crash Rescue Work of the British Fire Service

Images of Fire

Living Dangerously – Firefighters

FIREFIGHTER!

*The Drama and Humour of a
Dangerous Profession*

Neil Wallington

Firestorm Publications

For Tom

British Library Cataloguing in Publication Data
CIP Catalogue Record for this book is available from the British Library
ISBN 1 874365 01 6
© Neil Wallington 1992
Cover Photographs: West Yorkshire Fire Service and London Fire Brigade

Second Impression 1993

FIRESTORM PUBLICATIONS
PO Box 3
Budleigh Salterton
Devon, EX9 6YY
England

Typeset by The Charlesworth Group, UK, 0484 517077
Printed and bound by Antony Rowe Ltd, Eastbourne

Contents

Acknowledgements

In the preparation of this book, I must first acknowledge the ready assistance provided to me by a number of friends with whom I have served these past years, many who shared my firefighting adventures with me.

My appreciation is also due to the staff of both the London Fire Brigade library, and the Fire Service College library, and to a number of fellow Chief Fire Officer colleagues who have given me access to their photographic resources, and generally aided me in my writing task.

Finally, I owe a most enormous debt of gratitude to my very dear wife Susie. Often on my return from a major fire she has had to contend with the lingering aroma of smoke on my uniform, and a telephone which so often seemed to call me to battle at 3 am in the morning.

Throughout the writing of 'Firefighter!', Susie has given me the most tremendous inspiration as I have relived a little of the drama and humour of my fire service years, and my very special thanks are due to her for all splendid support.

NEIL WALLINGTON
Ebford
Exeter, Devon.

Foreword

At first glance it may seem somewhat unusual that a policeman should be asked to write the foreword to a book written by a fireman about the fire service. But, as both Neil Wallington and I know, there are many similarities in the two professions: the demands, the drama, the danger, the dedication, the times of agony but also the camaraderie and the humour. Both professions are committed to serving the public, and Neil Wallington's account, mostly from his own experiences, shows most vividly how the men and women of the fire brigades of this country serve their public, from dealing with fires in dustbins, through rescuing people trapped in buckets, lifts and mincing machines, to those incidents where all too often, while carrying out their life saving duties, they tragically lose their own.

My own personal experiences of the firefighters of this country range from boyhood memories of the unpaid volunteers in my Kentish village during the Second World War, to the many times when the police and fire services have worked together in London, particularly during the IRA bombing campaign of 1974–75 when a great number of terrorist devices were detonated. Most of those incidents needed close co-operation between fire, police and other emergency services so that evidence was preserved but the risk of fire was eliminated and lives were saved.

Many are the cups of tea I've had in fire stations on wet and bitterly cold nights when I first started street duty as a police constable in London. I remember too on my very first tour of night duty finding a smouldering dustbin in a doorway only a couple of hundred yards away from Rosebery Avenue fire station. I pulled the bin out to the centre of the pavement, strolled into the fire station and asked to borrow a fire extinguisher; they kindly said they would deal with it.

I had got no more than thirty yards down the road, when I heard the clanging of bells and saw three fire engines with half-dressed firemen hanging on to them race out of the station and pass me. I concluded that I would have to deal with my now well-burning dustbin myself. You can imagine my surprise when the fire engines skidded to a halt, water hoses magically and instantaneously appeared in the hands of the firemen and great jets of water were directed onto my dustbin, which was lifted from the ground by the force and, it seemed, swept away before my very eyes.

The fire was out but what had I done? Had I misled them into thinking it was dangerous and about to explode? The answer seemed to be in Governmental guidance which recommended that three appliances, for safety reasons, should attend every call. I learned a very important lesson that night, and later in my career I was to witness how valuable that guidance was.

It was just a few weeks after that incident that I was called early one evening to a fire in a school; it is customary for the police officer who attends to obtain a short comment from the senior fire officer present, and I have never forgotten the name of the officer I recorded on that occasion. It was Station Officer Fourt-Wells and it was to feature some time later during the reporting of a dreadful fire in Smithfield when he and another fireman lost their lives.

They are the times when members of the public, as well as those of us who are fellow professionals in the other emergency services, have it brought home to us, most forcibly, that fighting fires can be a very dangerous and, indeed, sometimes fatal occupation. Although such fatalities are all too frequent, fortunately they are not daily occurrences because of the fire officers' high levels of training and skills.

The fire service, although often exciting, can sometimes be routinely unexciting – there needs to be times of safety and comparative calm when one pauses for breath, presses the uniform, trains, and polishes up the brasses. But if it's never without its tragedies, it is also, fortunately, never without its humour. In this latest of Neil Wallington's books on the fire service, in which he served and which he loves so much, one will find a potpourri of it all, the tragic, the dramatic, the heroic, the humorous, the everyday stuff of firefighting, and the unforgettable.

As well as appealing to serving and retired firemen and women, the book will assuredly be enjoyed by ordinary readers who simply want to know something more about the fire service. It may also leave the reader asking for more and I hope Neil is able to provide just that in the future.

SIR PETER IMBERT, QPM,
*Commissioner of Police
of the Metropolis*

Introduction

I believe it fair to say that there can be few practical professions which bring such intense and lasting job satisfaction as that of being a firefighter. In fact, when I joined the fire service over 28 years ago, one of my early expectations was to become part of a team of professionals who, in part, were rewarded by the often successful outcome of their firefighting and rescue efforts. During my career in what is probably one of the most dangerous occupations on earth, I have tackled fires, both large and small, in locations as varied as the West End of London to the valleys of South Wales, and from the sunny Sussex downlands to the English Riviera of the South West.

Sometimes the outbreak of fire has been relatively straightforward to contain and extinguish. On other occasions, small fires have quickly developed into conflagrations of enormous energy, each frighteningly intimidating to every firefighter close to the scene.

It is a staggering fact that over £1,000 million literally goes up in smoke each year in the United Kingdom and around 800 men, women and children perish annually in the most tragic circumstances in fires, most asphyxiated by thick smoke long before flames claim their helpless bodies.

Over my firefighting years, there has also been a quite enormous growth in the amount of non-fire rescue and emergency '999' calls handled by fire brigades. These calls include dealing with road crashes where driver and passengers are trapped, making safe leaking toxic chemicals, lift rescues, and a whole variety of mishaps involving mechanical failures and accidents.

At these types of calls, I have frequently been witness

to a fair share of human drama on motorways and rural lanes alike, as well as being part of a team of firefighters which has rescued children or animals from varied predicaments such as high rock ledges or from the depths of foul smelling disused wells. Thankfully there have been so many happy outcomes to '999' calls, such as where a terrified child has been snatched to safety from a smoke filled bedroom, or when a family is finally cut free and gently eased out of the crumpled and bloodstained wreckage of their car. However, there are sadly many instances where despite all the skills and sophisticated equipment of the fire service, death and suffering are never far removed from a firefighter's life.

Early on in my career I learnt to become a veritable jack of all trades and in a sense, part engineer, chemist, electrician, doctor and nurse, psychologist, as well as a hydraulics expert – able to move vast quantities of water from one point to another in very quick time.

Another necessary attribute of a firefighter is the ready ability to respond at high speed as a disciplined team around the clock in all extremes of weather. Being part of such an organisation also demands a very special sense of humour. Surely few other professions can exist where that camaraderie and the ability to smile at oneself and fellow colleagues is of such paramount and vital importance as it is in the fire service. Although a firefighter does have to learn to regularly work amid scenes of human death and injury, this finely developed sense of humour helps to bind a team of rescuers together as I have often seen.

This collection of anecdotal and reflective accounts of my experiences covers almost three decades and draws upon both the humourous as well as the deeply serious side of a firefighter's work, in which the lessons of fire safety and accident prevention are clear for all to see.

This, indeed, is the story of some of the work of the nation's premier emergency organisation as it goes about its increasingly challenging, dangerous, and above all, life preserving task.

1
Footing the Ladder

My interest in a fire service career goes back to an uncle and also a family friend who had both served in the London Fire Service throughout the Second World War, and thus endured the London Blitz of 1940–41 and the flying bomb and rocket attacks of 1944–45. Each of these Blitz veterans occasionally, yet modestly, regaled me with fiery tales of wartime firefighting, which gradually aroused a keenness in the fire service in an impressionable ten year old.

In addition, whilst at school I shared a number of years with a close friend whose father was an officer in the then Croydon Fire Brigade. His family home was in the curtilage of one of that brigade's fire stations, at Woodside. Thus I never missed the opportunity to visit my friend's home and avail myself of the chance to inspect the two highly polished red fire engines which always seemed poised with all doors ajar, ready to roar into life at a moments notice. The two machines were surrounded in the fire engine bays by the crew's fire kit; pairs of fire boots and leggings, tunics and fire helmets, each positioned strategically by their owner ready to aid a speedy turnout to the scene of the next emergency '999' call.

The spotless engine house of the fire station had a distinct aroma of brass and floor polish about it and the presence of two shiny brass poles in opposite corners made it a quite magical place for a young boy to be.

If I were lucky, one of my frequent visits would coincide with the firemen's drill period in the yard when in awe, I watched them pull ladders off their fire engines, connect up hoses, and don breathing apparatus to deal with the most awful and masochistic, yet imaginary fires in the drill tower in the yard.

Set against this background it was not surprising therefore, that as I approached eighteen years of age, the
minimum age of appointment as a firefighter, I considered
a fire service career above all else. Unfortunately, even in
those days the number of vacancies due to natural wastage
was very small and the London Fire Brigade, then covering
the old London County Council area, had a long waiting
list for places on their basic recruits' course. London was,
as now, the largest fire brigade in the United Kingdom
and being London born I dearly wanted to be a London
fireman.

As a result I also placed my name on the waiting list
of Croydon Fire Brigade, then a brigade of four fire stations and some 172 officers and firemen, protecting a
county borough of about 250,000 population. I did this
in the early months of 1963, in the knowledge that under
a forthcoming reorganisation, Croydon and several other
small brigades, including East Ham and West Ham,
together with parts of surrounding county brigades would
be merging in 1965 with the London Fire Brigade. The
LFB would then form a much enlarged fire service for the
capital and Greater London area.

There was in this intervening period of waiting for
selection as a fireman, the opportunity to enrol in the
Auxiliary Fire Service. This body had been originally
established in 1938 to form a wartime supplementary part-
time firefighting reserve. As war was declared in September
1939, many Auxiliary Fire Service (AFS) firemen and
women joined the strengths of regular brigades and in
fact both my uncle and the family friend, now partly
responsible for my career ambitions, had become wartime
London firefighters via this AFS route.

After hostilities ceased, the AFS crews were kept in
training on a part-time voluntary basis on a national
scheme which had its origins in the Cold War of that
time. In event of war the AFS would, as in 1939, be
expected to provide a major back up to the professional
firefighting forces. By the early sixties, Croydon Fire Brig-

ade had about 100 AFS volunteers with their own dark green Bedford fire engines, known affectionally as 'green goddesses'. The AFS operated nationally rather like the Territorial Army with weekly drill nights and weekend exercises, and with its own rank structure and organisation within the control and broad umbrella of the regular fire service.

Thus in the summer of 1963, I joined the Croydon AFS as a 'stop gap' measure pending my ultimate call up for the professional service. After the issue of my uniform and completion of a very basic training course spread over several weekends which introduced me to hose running, pitching and working off ladders and pump operating, I then turned out for the Monday night three hour continuation training at the AFS fire station and headquarters in Old Town, Croydon.

The AFS fire station which housed three dark green AFS fire engines and several other support vehicles was an undistinguished three bay building set at the rear of a large drill yard, one corner of which was dominated by a seven floor drill tower. The drill facilities were also used by the professional crews based in the adjacent Old Town fire station. This was a handsome new structure built only five years before and housed six gleaming red fire engines in its bays. At one end of the complex was the operational headquarters and administrative offices of the Croydon brigade including a control room where all '999' fire calls were received for the entire Croydon county borough area.

Although AFS personnel thus shared a common training and drill area with the regular firefighters, there was in reality little contact between the AFS volunteers and the duty shift of professional firemen who manned the red appliances based at Old Town which protected the central area of Croydon. They were, of course, nicknamed the 'red riders' and were a source of unbridled envy to me during AFS drill nights when they would be concluding their various training exercises in the drill yard as we AFS types arrived for our evening stint. Even apart from their drill sessions, there was always some activity going on within the regular fire station so tantalisingly close.

My envy intensified when one or more red fire engines would spectacularly turn out to a '999' emergency in full view of AFS volunteers at drill during our evening session. Each time I watched the drama and absorbed the noise and spectacle of a 'red' turnout at close hand, there was never any doubt as to what my vocation in life was to be. Not an AFS drill night went by without me yearning to have my name reach the top of the waiting list for recruits to the professional fire service.

Whilst AFS duties were generally mundane, I managed to absorb all the technical theory I could relating to firefighting, and naturally found every minute of the practical training and lectures on AFS pumps and equipment to be a very useful prelude to becoming a regular fireman. Apart from this, there was also a very pleasant and active social life within the AFS organisation at Croydon. Amongst the 100 active members of the AFS were about ten lady members, some who were either married or engaged to AFS firemen. The firewomen's AFS role was primarily communications, light driving and some administration. I do not recall any in those days who wanted to take on firefighting duties which in 1963 really was an exclusive male preserve.

Sometimes, however, AFS life could be quite exciting, even if in a perverse way. On one occasion soon after I had qualified to ride as a crew member, I and three other colleagues were manning an AFS Land Rover en route for a Sunday morning water relaying exercise in the Woodside area of Croydon. Quite without warning, the driver of the Land Rover decided to have some fun. As we approached a series of traffic lights at red in central Croydon, he switched on the vehicle's diminutive electric warning bell and blue beacon, and accelerated towards the complex junctions ahead. I was quite unprepared for this and along with the other two firemen in the back of the Land Rover, hung on for grim death. We roared through four sets of traffic lights with our tinny bell ringing out pitifully and I glimpsed at least three cars which had the green light, screech to a sudden halt as we flashed through. The Land Rover was but a personnel carrier and certainly not a first line fire engine and I could not imagine what was going on. When we arrived at our destination, I presumed that every ride to a fire must be as hectic as this one had been. The Land Rover driver had a certain grin on his face and had I not been a new recruit, I might have been tempted to pass comment on his driving.

That this particular AFS driver never killed or injured anyone was little short of a miracle for I soon discovered two things. The first was that he carried out this stunt fairly regularly, especially on Sundays when the traffic was somewhat thinner. The second point of note was that our frustrated fire engine driver had twice been turned down for entry into the professional fire service.

Indeed, not all AFS personnel were set on a regular career as many clearly would not have satisfied the strict medical standards required for the full time service, especially those relating to eyesight where good vision without glasses was a must, and a minimum height of 5 feet 7 inches which was also a prerequisite. The majority of Croydon AFS firemen with whom I trained alongside during 1963–64 were, I suspect, community minded people who were attracted to the certain glamour of a firefighter's uniform. Probably most would also admit that being in the AFS was the next best thing to being a 'red rider'.

Another feature of AFS routine that gave me considerable anticipatory delight during my period of waiting for my regular 'call up' papers was the occasional large fire in the Croydon area which happened to coincide with AFS training nights. When such large incidents occured, the Chief Fire Officer had authorised some AFS crews to attend to supplement the firefighting effort and to gain some valuable experience under the watchful eye of regular officers.

The very first such fire that I was fortunate to attend

took place during a wet evening in August 1963. Whilst we were in the middle of pitching ladders into the drill tower and getting hose lines to work on some imaginary conflagration, we became aware that the call out bells were ringing in the regular station across the yard. After about thirty seconds had elapsed, we could see the crews running to the appliances and the first blue flashing beacons burst into life as two red fire engines roared off to the '999' call, bells clanging a warning into the damp night air.

Croydon Fire Brigade had been one of the first in the country to fit an experimental set of electric two tone horns to one of its fire engine fleet to supplement the traditional fire bell. When we heard the call out bells again ringing only a minute or so after the first turnout, and soon heard the unfamiliar do–dah, do–dah of the experimental pump going out, I suspected a large fire might be developing somewhere.

And so it was. Within a further five minutes or so, the telephone in the watchroom of the AFS station rang and those of us crewing the 'first' green goddess and in earshot felt a surge of nervous energy. Was an AFS crew going to be turned out also?

Whilst the question flashed through my mind, the AFS call out system rang out as the Croydon Brigade's control room ordered one AFS pump to a large fire in a woodyard at Kings Road, Anerley, close to the edge of the Croydon county borough area. Like Battle of Britain pilots, the six man crew of the green goddess swung up into the high crew cab as the fire engine roared into life, and was quickly away on a journey of about six miles.

Of the crew, I was the only 'rookie' who had yet to attend a real working job. My nervousness and apprehension was high as the green fire engine swung hard left out of the fire station complex into the early evening traffic in Old Town. Centrifugal force threw me unexpectedly right into my two crew colleagues sitting on that side. We were all trying to get rigged into our fire kit which consisted of boots and thigh length black leggings, a double breasted melton cloth tunic around which went a webbing belt with axe pouch and axe. Then there was the fire helmet.

None of this would have been easy to achieve quickly standing still and upright, but in the narrow confines of a crew cab it was an absolute nightmare. No matter how I tried I could not engage the right hooks and buttons which, of course, so easily slipped into place on every drill night parade. Worst still was the clear evidence that my experienced colleagues all completed this ritual dressing in about one minute flat by which time I had only sorted my boots and leggings out.

As I rigged, I was pleased to realise that unlike the dangerous manner of the Land Rover episode, this driver was obviously very aware of other road users and his anticipation and skillful handling of the rather lumbering Bedford fire engine was positively impressive. Within a minute of the turnout, we had almost halted at red traffic lights until our driver was sure all other vehicles had seen and heard us. Despite this, the raucous sound of the hand bell of the green goddess being rung with great gusto by our Sub Officer in charge in the front seat alongside the driver, added a constant urgency to our passage through the traffic. The appliance seemed to be constantly driven very hard in each gear with the petrol engine revving noisily almost to the limit of its power range. Once I had finally completed my dressing, the Sub Officer suddenly paused from his bell ringing and looked over his shoulder at me.

'You OK?' he enquired.

I nodded in assent but felt far from composed as I wondered what lay ahead. Just how had our Sub managed to get rigged before me *and* ring that bell? Then as we started to approach the scene we were forced to slow up due to traffic congestion although I could now see several policeman waving us down the outside of the traffic queue.

There ahead of us and completely dominating the entire

area was a deep pulsating orange glow which sent showers of sparks spiralling up into the night sky like swarms of agitated glowworms. It was a memorable sight and I felt like a knight going into battle.

In the event, the fire at Kings Road woodyard was something of an anticlimax. By the time we arrived, the regular crews there before us already had several lines of hose to work and had almost surrounded the blazing contents of the timber merchant's. Even so, thick smoke and sparks were being blown all around us and it was intermittently hard to see and breathe.

Our Sub Officer told us to wait by the green goddess now parked behind six red fire engines, as he went off to report to the senior officer in charge. He was soon back to detail us to work in support of other fire crews working water jets at the back of the largest timber stacks.

It was still pretty hot from the radiated heat from the fire as we made our way carefully through the swirling smoke. The seat of the fire appeared to be very deep, right inside the timber stacks, some of which had collapsed inwards. Steam was now beginning to mix with the smoke and the darkness did not help my confidence, although part of my basic training had included the principles of moving in smoke by keeping as low as possible to seek all the available oxygen. Nevertheless, there was by now a lot of hose in use, laid out like some gigantic cobweb network, which was feeding the water jets via street hydrants and the fire pumps.

Eventually, my crew located the rear of the timber stacks and joined up with about fifteen other firemen already playing cooling water onto the seat of the fire, as well as the walls of the buildings close behind the wood-yard which had, at one stage, also been seriously threat-ened by the spread of fire. The water sprays being played onto these buildings almost immediately turned to steam, so hot was the brickwork of these adjacent properties. Working in teams, we gently eased the heavy hose lines forward and supported their pulsating weight as those firemen at the nozzle end slowly and carefully moved forward as they progressively extinguished the fire. These firefighters not only had the worst of the heat, smoke, sparks and steam to contend with, but also had to combat the powerful jet reaction of a high pressure water stream throwing over a hundred gallons of water per minute into the inferno.

As we worked down the back of the wood stack, parts of the area started to be floodlit as other firefighters erected portable lighting sets from one of the support vehicles. Very much more steam was now in evidence as the smoke started to turn a lighter colour but it was still very uncomfortable, what with my tunic now being soaking wet from all the flying water droplets as well as the swirling smoke catching my breath and causing me to retch frequently. My eyes were streaming continuously and I really began to feel that I had come through my baptism by fire pretty well.

The intense firefighting effort went on progressively all round the site for about an hour and during this time there was some considerable exchange of banter between crews from the different fire stations attending the fire. Interestingly, because this incident had occurred close to the edge of Croydon's boundary, some of the reinforcing fire engines had come from the London Fire Brigade and Kent also. What was impressive was how all the crews merged almost imperceptably into one force at the scene.

At about midnight, the order came to shut off and begin the protracted task of reducing the hose lines down to those sufficient for damping down purposes only. There followed a concerted effort to shut down street fire hydrants, disconnect and unravel the tangle of hose lines laid out at such speed earlier in the evening. I really had not noticed how the past three hours had flown by, so great was my absorption with the task and experience at hand. Neither did I realise just how weary I was until I pitched in to help roll up the many heavy, dripping wet, and very dirty 75 foot lengths of hose used at the fire. This was a far from easy task in which one had to guard against finger nail and knuckle damage. At gone midnight I also discovered that this task, like many others, was far more difficult than when carried out in the drill yard!

Even at this late hour, there was still a sizeable crowd of onlookers watching operations going on and these spectators were mostly concentrated and marshalled by policemen at the entrance to the woodyard in Kings Road. As I came close to the crowd during my hose rolling, I suddenly felt very proud of being a grimy and sweaty fireman who had played a small part in getting the fire under control.

My pride was, however, suddenly punctured as in bending over to start to roll up yet another length of hose, my fire helmet fell off into a very dirty pool of water blackened by the products of combustion. There was a ripple of laughter from the crowd, not least when I quickly retrieved my dripping helmet and replaced it back to front! All the AFS crews wore a firefighting uniform that was almost identical to that of regular crews except for 'AFS' flashes on both shoulders and on fire helmets. I wondered in the darkness if any of the spectators had noticed that I was not a professional.

It was a more sedate drive back to Croydon AFS fire station at about 0200 hours after my crew and I had gathered up all the hose and other equipment that had been in use. Behind us we left several regular crews to continue with damping down and turning over the hundreds of tons of charred and still smouldering timber to prevent re-ignition. I had yet to discover the delights of this mundane, dirty and physically tiring yet important work, especially at such an awful hour.

Once back at the AFS station, I wearily hung my dripping wet fire kit up in the drying room before taking a quick shower where the benison of the hot water was indescribably wonderful. Then I booked off duty and headed for home and bed. As I did so, I could not get rid of the pungent smoky aroma or the taste of the fire.

It was a smell I was shortly to come to know only too well, for several weeks later came the papers summoning me for an assessment interview at Croydon Fire Brigade headquarters for appointment into the professional fire service.

2
Learning the Ropes

From then on, events moved apace and a fortnight later my recruiting interview at Croydon HQ, on the second floor of Croydon fire station, was a pretty summary affair. It was clear that the two officers had my AFS probationary reports in front of them.

When asked the inevitable question – why did I want to give up my secure and well paid sales job in the motor trade to become a fireman, I felt I could answer with some conviction. For had I not by then been an AFS member for almost two years, with a reasonable idea of what the job was all about? I really did seek an outdoor career, and an exciting and glamorous one which I was sure was to be found around those gleaming red fire engines. The danger and hazards of the profession just did not register very prominently.

Nor did the chores which offset the excitement of rushing to fires. When questioned, I assured one of the interviewing officers that I did not mind cleaning lavatories and doing other menial domestic chores on the fire station, which in those days was all an accepted part of the 'self sufficiency' of the fire service where many firefighters were ex-national servicemen who were well used to such tasks.

The starting pay was the princely sum of £830 per annum, well below the industrial average of that time. After passing a stiff medical examination, I was assigned a starting date in December 1964, on an eleven week course at the London Fire Brigade's training school at Southwark, close by the River Thames. Croydon, like many smaller brigades did not train their own firefighters, preferring to send them to one of the large regional recruit schools such as that at Southwark.

This basic training gave a recruit an insight into the theory of firefighting, although the emphasis was understandably on the practical aspect. At Southwark over the weeks, raw recruits were shaped and moulded into firemen. The instructors unravelled the many mysteries of hose, pumps and primers, knots and lines, sprinkler systems, foam equipment, extinguishers and a host of other firefighting subjects. A recruit formed part of a squad of trainees who then learnt to manhandle a fireman's basic rescue ladder – the three-quarter ton wheeled escape. At rescue situations, this ladder was quickly pulled off its carrying fire engine and wound up manually as required to its maximum working height of 50 feet. Its use was discontinued in the 1980s in favour of lighter alloy ladders. Recruits also learnt to use the 35-foot general purpose extension ladder in drill situations. After the first week on these ladders, I looked up to the upper floors of the drill tower with a mixture of apprehension and awe at other more advanced squads using hook ladders high above the drill yard.

A hook ladder was made of ash, 13 feet long and only ten inches wide, weighing a mere 35 pounds. At its top it had a metal hook with serrated teeth on the underside. This ladder was normally used in a vertical position with the hook put through a window or over a sill – the ladder thus hung suspended. A firefighter then climbed up to the next floor, pulled the ladder up and pitched it to the floor above and so on. In this manner, the face of a building could be scaled irrespective of parked cars and other obstacles which could prevent the use of a wheeled escape. In some extreme cases, rescued persons had themselves been guided down these ladders to safety below. However, due to their very rare operational use allied to several fatal accidents during training sessions, by the mid 1970s most brigades in the United Kingdom had phased out the hook ladder.

Like the rest of my fellow recruits in the squad, I was trembling when our instructor, Sub Officer Groves, assembled all fifteen of us around the base of the six floor drill tower ready for our first lesson in hook ladders. Bill Groves was a thickset Londoner, a fire officer of considerable experience and perhaps less inclined to shout and bawl at his charges than most of the other instructors. First, he demonstrated how the ladder was lifted into the vertical position and how the long hook at the top was placed into the cill of the first floor window. He then climbed up and down the first floor several times showing how easy it was, providing the left hand and left foot, then right hand and right foot, moved in synchronised time. One by one, we tried the fearsome ladder up to the first floor; it did not seem too bad after all.

'Wait till you go higher – its terrible,' said one tenth-week recruit to me after this first encounter. For although I had long become accustomed to AFS ladders (none over 30 foot), hook ladders were the real fear of all recruits.

And terrible it was. One cold and windy morning of the second week of the course came the session when the Sub Officer coaxed us all, turn by turn, to sit in at the first floor window, then lift the single hook ladder out and gingerly raise it six inches at a time to hook into the window above. This was no easy feat with a strong wind blowing and arm muscles aching as we tried to control the ladder overhead. Worse was to follow. When my turn came I pitched the ladder up, then grasped the bottom of it and climbed out, trembling and fearful to look down. As I ascended to the second floor up the vertical climb, the ladder seemed to vibrate throughout its flimsy length. When my eyes came level with the sill of the window, I saw only two of the serrated teeth biting into the timberwork. Realising that very little was suspending me 40 feet above the ground, I thought, 'I'll never make it any higher.' Others in the squad apparently felt the same, but over several following sessions a little confidence started to emerge.

'Come on man, up you go, left hand and foot together. Keep going. That's it. Up and in you go!'

Every time I swung my leg into the safety and security of the drill tower levels, I was sweating profusely, my heart pounding and arms aching from pushing the hook ladder up.

From this stage the squad slowly progressed to the full two-man, two-ladder drill, in which the fireman on the upper ladder was suspended from a metal ring on his ladder by a safety belt; this left his hands free to take hold of the lower ladder when it was passed up to him.

At this point however, one of the squad met with real difficulty. Keith was probably the quietest member of our course, a ginger haired serious looking lad of twenty-one. He had had some problems earlier with coming to terms with hook ladder work, especially when Sub Officer Groves took us above the second floor for the first time. On this morning Keith froze at this level, unable to command his mind and body to climb out and go up higher. Rather than shout to Keith from the ground, Bill Groves dismissed the rest of the squad for ten minutes for a breather, went up the tower on the hook ladder and sat alongside Keith, then went up and down several times himself. He then held the bottom of Keith's hook ladder as the reluctant recruit struggled out into the position ready to climb up. I watched this scene from the window of an equipment store below and saw Keith's demon slowly being exorcised. By the end of the week, Keith had conquered his fear of heights and my respect for our instructor had grown considerably.

But it was not all drill sessions. Whilst at training school recruits learnt the physics and chemistry of fire extinction, of pressure and vacuum, and the other associated sciences of getting vast quantities of water from one place to another. There was the basics of fire service law and the many procedures in force, both on a fire station and at emergency calls, as well as something of the history and tradition of the service.

There was also a new language of expressions to learn. In Victorian times, because of the duty system which demanded that firemen live on a fire station and be on call twenty-four hours a day, and the physical strength and discipline needed to work at heights, the London Brigade only recruited ex Royal Navy and other seamen and with them came some of their terminology. Hence going up a ladder was 'going aloft', a hose hauled up the face of a building was 'hauled aloft' and anything not secured properly was said to have 'come adrift'. Fire stations were even referred to in this maritime parlance as when a particular station was said to be a 'happy' ship.

Whilst I had had some basic theoretical training during my AFS service, it was at Southwark that I really started to learn the subject of 'firemanship'. This was all about applying the basic practical skills and techniques of fire-fighting to any given fire situation, especially with an ever present emphasis on safety. How to move on fire weak-ened stairs be they of timber or stone construction, working in smoke, ventilating smoke filled buildings, the quickest use of hose lines, and knowing the early signs of the collapse of a structure, was just a very little of the wealth of 'firemanship' knowledge that a firefighter was expected to absorb. And once posted to a fire station, every '999' fire or emergency attended meant an oppor-tunity to build upon this important facet of the profession.

By the third week of the course, most of my fellow recruits were still having some difficulty or other. For me, it was the sheer pace and pressure of the course timetable, cramming notes down during lectures and then rushing to change into fire kit for a outside practical session in the pouring rain. For others it was the severe and endless regimentation and discipline which, quite frankly, some recruits had clearly not been used to either at school or in their civilian job. Then there were several, like Keith, who were not too happy during the ladder drills of the first fortnight, which were confined to the third floor of the tower, about forty feet up. The prospect of going to the top of the tower – some 80 feet high – as the course progressed was daunting, but at least I had my AFS background although I did not admit that this had never taken me beyond the third floor either!

All the intensity of work, uncertainty and fear at Southwark was offset by the various instructors who all seemed characters of great stature and experience. They worked us like beavers, and had the answers for everything. They coaxed, cajoled, and coerced us into some semblance of order, turning us slowly at first, then more obviously as the course advanced, into thinking and confident members of a crew.

Not that the course did not have its lighter moments. All the instructors had a little of the comedian in them and Bill Groves was no exception. During practical drill sessions which were going badly wrong, he would often have a marvellous turn of phrase that could make us cry with laughter, thus easing the tension of the moment. Such ribaldry would frequently concern one's paternity or anatomy.

Certainly in those pre equal opportunity days there was no restriction as to what rude comments could be made about a recruit fireman's potential by an instructor. This is far removed from today's scene where with the advent of female firefighters, the service has almost gone to the far extreme to ensure that equal opportunities are practised.

Southwark instructors also had the knack of using drill sessions to emphasise that fire service equipment was expensive and had to be carefully handled. On one occasion early on in the course, I was one of a four man team starting an extension ladder drill. Practical sessions in the drill yard were always a cue for the heavens to open and this day was no exception. The drill involved taking the ladder off a fire engine with each corner of the ladder being supported by one of us. In slow time this was easily mastered but we had advanced to doing every drill in double quick time. As I took my share of the weight of the ladder and we started running towards the drill tower, I felt my grip slipping on the wet surface of the ladder sides. Before I could shout a warning, the ladder slid from my grasp, and the corner of the ladder crashed to the ground and was noisily drawn along with the impetus of the drill.

'Don't damage that bloody ladder! Don't you dare damage that ladder!' shouted Bill Groves in a rare display of real displeasure.

I recall that the drill was stopped right there and we had to go back through it all a number of times again until I could demonstrate beyond any doubt that I had learnt the technique of carrying a ladder properly and safely. My crew were quite exhausted by the time we were finished, but it must have had its effect for never again in all my service years, did I ever drop an extension ladder.

My recruits training took place during the winter of 1964 which was very wet and cold with a fair amount of snow and ice. If the snow had fallen overnight, one of the recruits' first tasks was to sweep and salt the entire drill yard before the day's programme could begin. The area was about the size of three or four football pitches but with about 200 recruits in training, manpower was not a problem. Nor would the adverse weather affect the daily routine of physical training when several squads would cavort through set exercises designed to keep us firefighting fit. In reality, I think we were a pretty fit bunch anyway and although being in shorts and singlet first thing in the morning did put colour into one's cheeks, by the end of the third week or so, any surplus fat or indolent muscle had been banished, such was the overall pace of the course.

Another lesson well learnt by us all early on was the eternal quest on top of all else to keep spick and span, both in uniform and in person. Any spare time at Southwark if not revising for the regular assessments was spent in polishing our leather boots until they had a mirror finish, or ironing trousers so that the creases were knife sharp. Hair length too, was never allowed to grow very much whilst at Southwark. Indeed, several recruits who turned up on the first morning with less than a short back and sides were promptly sent to the barbers a few streets away for another haircut, this time to London Fire Brigade specification!

As the course progressed came a real baptism in smoke and although I had attended a few fires whilst in the AFS, I had not fought a fire at close quarters *inside* a building. Hence I recall that this experience was unforgettable if only for the physical discomforture it entailed. Part of the basement of the training school consisted of a number of specially constructed inter-connecting rooms, crawling galleries and search areas normally used by qualified firemen undergoing breathing apparatus training. This convoluted complex was known as the 'rat run'.

One day around week seven, Sub Officer Groves prepared and lit a smouldering fire of rags and wood chips in a brazier down in the 'rat run' and allowed it to burn for about ten minutes. After a briefing as to the general layout of the basement, we went down the stairs through several doors and were suddenly enveloped in thick, pungent smoke. Although we were accompanied by instructors, I don't think any of us were prepared for the ordeal. We scrambled down onto our tummies as taught to seek what oxygen was left in the area, clinging to each other for mutual comfort and security. We coughed and spluttered our way through the thick drifting haze, lit only by the flickering malevolent glow from the fire in a small adjacent room. As we passed it, our eyes streamed and our hearts pounded as we made our way through the complex.

When after about three or four minutes we all broke out into the cool, clear air of the drill yard, it was if the ordeal had lasted for hours. Most of us retched with the discomfort we had gone through, whilst comforting ourselves that at last we were real 'smoke eaters'. Probably only I and one other ex London AFS recruit on the course – Ron Bentley – knew that this very brief encounter was only a taste of the normal operational world of a firefighter.

Looking back after almost thirty years, it is incredible that this torture by smoke was the commonplace method used to give recruits a feel of the enemy. There was, I recall, some sort of smoke evacuation system in case of emergency but I often wonder what the Health and Safety Commission would have made of this widespread practice of earlier years, had the Commission been in being all those years ago. In those days, a recruit was expected to get some eighteen months fire experience as a crew member before going back to Southwark for a one week breathing apparatus (BA) course. Once thus qualified, a firefighter could don BA if the conditions were judged to warrant it. As most fire engines then only carried three BA sets for a crew of up to six firefighters, there was never enough BA for everyone. Not only that, but there was a belief amongst older firemen and officers at that time that part of being a good firefighter included being able to absorb plenty of smoke punishment at fires, rather than resort to the bother of artificial aids to respiration!

Fortunately, during my early years things started to change for the better, firstly with a far greater awareness of the respiratory hazards of burning plastics and their toxic smoke then becoming far more readily commonplace at fires. There then followed a programme to equip every pump with a full set of BA as well as there being far greater use at small fires of what is, in effect, a firefighter's life support system. As I was to find out repeatedly over my first few firefighting years, smoke is so toxic that it is sometimes necessary to wear BA even outside a building involved in fire. Smoke never loses its dark and swirling threat to a firefighter and on so many tragic occasions over almost three decades, I was to see that smoke is the real killer in fires, not the flames.

Yet another very memorable experience at training school was my first ride up a 100 foot Turntable Ladder (TL). These largest of British fire engines are used either as a rescue ladder or to project a water jet into a burning building from above. In addition, they could be used to give fire crews access onto roofs or into buildings at a high level. The ladder consisted of telescopic sections which could be rotated through a complete circle. Each of the squad had about a ten minute session at the top of the ladder which commenced with having to climb onto the housed ladder which rested flat in its travelling position. After I had reached the six inch wide step platform at the ladder head and clipped the safety belt on, I gave the ladder operator the 'ready' signal and held my breath. Suddenly, I heard the appliance's engine note rise as it took up the ladder drive, and without any warning the ladder started to lift me jerkily up into the vertical position. Whilst I was part prepared for this upward movement, I was not ready to be simultaneously shot up to 100 feet very quickly. This only took about fifteen seconds or so as the world below me diminished rapidly and I soared out above the Southwark rooftops and drilltowers. I was transfixed by the view until maximum height was reached with a slight bump. Only then did I look down through my feet at the tiny figures of my fellow recruits below, and only then did I realise that the whole five ton ladder section with me at the very top was swaying ever so gently in the light breeze. The lack of any sound sensation now was quite eerie until a voice broke out.

'Are you OK up there?'

It was a reassuring enquiry from the ladder operator over the intercom system from 100 feet down.

'Yes, I'm fine, I really am,' I replied, hopefully sounding far more confident than I actually was.

'Right, well 'old on tight then!' came the reply from down below.

The ladder again lurched into life, lifted me up slightly and then suddenly pitched forward and down over the rooftops below. Then even worse, the whole ladder started rotating around its base as I went further and further forward and down still at about 80 feet up. It was a 'white knuckle' ride to end them all. Then it was back up to 100 feet and another marvellous view out over towards the

Houses of Parliament one way, and St. Paul's in the other. It was quite an experience and although I subsequently came to serve on, and qualified as, a driver/operator at TL fire stations where I gained plenty of aerial experience, I never forgot that first dramatic brush with these massive fire engines.

In no time at all, the final recruits examination was upon the squad. Once the written sessions were completed it was the turn of us all to take to the drill yard at the Lambeth HQ of the London Fire Brigade to display our skills with the equipment. This lengthy practical session before a panel of examining officers included 'carry down' drill, in which each recruit took a turn not only to 'carry down' a body from the third floor level via a wheeled escape ladder, but also took a turn to be the body as well! This was far more scary than the actual carry itself, for one was simply perched over a colleague's back whilst resisting the temptation to hang on to some part of his uniform during the speedy descent.

The hook ladder sequence was both a one and two man drill. In the latter, I teamed up with Ron Bentley and all went well during the ascent until we reached the fifth floor, some 70 feet up. He was out on the top of the hook ladder already pitched up to the sixth floor, whilst I sat in the cill of the fifth floor proper. I passed the second hook ladder up to Ron above me whilst trying hard to demonstrate the correct and safe handling technique. As I did so, one of the ladder rounds (rungs) jammed into the hook of my hook belt and Ron above me pulled the ladder up so hard he nearly unseated me from my lofty perch. We finally sorted ourselves out after an embarrassing delay and as we both arrived breathlessly over the top parapet of the Lambeth tower, some eight floors up, we thought we had contributed little towards our final marks.

However, after a more controlled descent we each proceeded to other ladder and pump drills, including a knots and lines session where I had to show that I could tie the twenty four knots expected of a fireman, including some in the dark and behind my back. Finally, the hectic and strenuous day at Lambeth concluded with an individual interview with the panel of assessors which covered a whole range of firemanship questions.

That evening the entire squad took to the local hostelry to celebrate the end of the course. It was inevitably a night for celebration, for each of us knew that the introduction we had been given to the fire service and its teamwork and camaraderie was to be the whole basis for our future careers. I also knew that despite the harsh discipline and pace of training school, I was going to miss the place. Hence when we all turned out next morning for our passing out parade through some king sized hangovers, there was a certain sense of emotion allied to the achievement of completing the course itself. Before we went out to take part in the parade, we learnt our final course markings and to my incredulous delight I had achieved a very respectable total in all the various sections which gave me overall 1st place.

Thus during the passing out parade I had particular pleasure in being part of the senior squad, proudly rigged in full firefighting uniform which for weeks past had been endlessly polished in anticipation of the final day at Southwark. After the euphoria of the morning, it was time to say our farewells and these were not without a tear or two, so binding had the weeks of teamwork and reliance upon each other been.

We each piled our kit and ourselves into various fire service vans to be taken back to our respective operational fire station postings. As the transport taking three other Croydon firemen and myself back to our brigade drove through the arched entrance to Southwark training school and into the afternoon traffic, I sensed that my professional firefighting adventure was about to begin.

The Recruit on the Drill Tower

All right for him to shout at me,
I'm shaking like an Aspen leaf,
He's on the ground, I'm three floors up.
It's me not he will come to grief.

'Go on. Go up. Don't hesitate!'
I can't, I'll fall. I daren't look down.
I hear a thumping, tower shakes,
A hook goes past me, round by round.

He comes aloft, he wears a grin.
'Suppose you thought that I'm too old,
That only young like you can climb?
All men can climb if they are bold.'

And on he climbs, I follow suit,
Feel such a fool, his help I spurn.
My squad will laugh; I too will laugh,
For in a moment comes their turn.

Charles Clisby, Divisional Officer, London Fire Brigade.

3
First Fatalities

When I returned as a fully trained recruit firefighter to Croydon fire station in Old Town to where my permanent posting had now been confirmed, there was a little frustration awaiting me. I had been posted to one of the watches (or shifts) that manned the fire engines around the clock on a progressive rota system.

This meant that when I picked up the rota on the Friday of my return from Southwark training school, my watch had just come off duty and was now on a weekend off, leaving me to gaze at the five red fire appliances which I longed to ride. The duty watch seemed very organised for there on the first floor was a locker with 'Fireman Wallington' on it. Better still, on the ground floor amid the long line of neatly hung fire tunics, helmets and boots of the off duty crews close by the fire engine bays, was a peg waiting for my firefighting uniform. As I hung it up in the fashion of all the rest, there again was the unmistakable aroma of smoke and battles recently fought. As my own uniform merged with the long identical row, for the very first time I really did feel like a 'red rider'.

There was now nothing else to be done but to head off into the gathering evening to enjoy my weekend. But before I did, there was one other call to make. Still in my walking-out rig, which was rather inappropriately termed an 'undress' uniform, and pulling my peaked cap down to make me look even more like a guardsman, I marched across the empty drill yard towards the lights of the AFS fire station where my career had germinated almost two years ago.

Friday night was an AFS cleaning and maintenance evening and sure enough, there were a number of my past colleagues hard at the spit and polish. I tried hard to put on a superior air during my brief visit, which in retrospect was nothing less than blatant showmanship. But it did compensate a little for having to wait until after the weekend for my first duty as a 'red rider'.

On the following Monday, I duly reported to Old Town in good time and was warmly greeted by two other firemen – Ray and Malcolm – both in their late twenties. As my watch (or shift) started to noisily assemble for the 0900 hours roll call and parade in full firefighting uniform in front of the red fire engines, they all seemed a friendly lot.

The parade and roll call was taken by the watch commander, Station Officer Slade and included instructions as to which particular firefighters were allocated to crew the five fire engines, announcements as to road closures, the day's special routines and fire prevention visits to local industries during the afternoon.

Amid the two long lines of firefighters on parade were some obvious contrasting characters. The watch Sub Officer, the second in charge, was a swarthy and athletic looking six foot plus tower of a man, with a lovely droopy ginger moustache. At the other end of the physical scale was George Fisher, one of the three Leading Firemen. He was so short that he would never have satisfied the then recruiting height requirement of 5 foot 7 inches. But George had an impeccable firefighting pedigree, having served through the fire and drama of the London Blitz.

Over the next few weeks George acted as my mentor, as I absorbed the various routines of the fire station and the sometimes strict pattern of the training sessions which were every bit as intense as those at training school. Despite his diminutive stature and silver grey hair, George was a real terrier as he chased and chivied the younger firemen about their various maintenance and cleaning tasks on the station, and could clearly be very assertive when he needed to be.

Of the five fire engines at Old Town, two, the Pump

Escape and Pump, were pumping appliances of a type found on most fire stations. The Pump Escape carried a fifty foot wheeled escape ladder and the Pump several smaller conventional ladders. Both engines had 300 gallons of water on board feeding 240 feet of hose reel tubing on both sides. In addition each had 1,000 feet of rolled hose, breathing apparatus, extinguishers, ropes and lines, small tools and a host of other smaller items.

The third fire engine was a 100 foot Turntable Ladder identical to the one that had provided me with that memorable ten minutes at training school. Croydon also had an Emergency Tender based at Old Town and this was literally a travelling workshop that attended emergencies such as road crashes where its generator, power tools and lighting equipment made it an invaluable type of fire engine. Lastly, there was a Foam Tender used specifically in the event of fire and spillages of large quantities of flammable fuels.

On this first morning as a professional fireman, Old Town fire station with its immaculately clean floors and neatness everywhere, allied to its five well polished fire engines had the feel of a palace about it. And all the time, that first '999' call might come in.

However, the morning moved on with two hours of intense ladder and pump drill around the large practice tower. During the drill, I underwent my initiation as I was sent alone up into the third floor into which was directed three water jets each pumping about 100 gallons per minute! It was a deluge not to be forgotten and even after my return to the drill yard level, water poured out of my tunic for minutes after as I squelched around – the water baby of the watch.

After a warming shower and dry clothes, it was lunchtime and there had still not been a callout, but just as the watch were settling down to their meal in the dining room, the station bells noisily rang their call to arms.

It was momentary chaos. Chairs were pushed back, and cutlery clattered down as the watch stampeded to the two polehouses for the drop down the shiny poles into the fire engine bays below. Each large bay door crashed open as the drivers starting up their vehicles. Blue shafts of light from the revolving beacons shimmered around the engine bays like laser beams. As each fireman frantically started to get rigged in uniform, the indicator panels over each bay door quickly flashed up 'Pump Escape' and 'Pump' to show which appliances were being despatched according to the type of emergency. It was a call to a house fire near East Croydon railway station. Utter bliss – I was crewing the Pump.

Amid a slamming of cab doors and shouts of 'all clear' to each driver the two red fire engines, a Dennis and a Bedford, roared out into Old Town, swung hard right and accelerated off towards East Croydon. I had managed to get into my boots and tunic before climbing on board, and at last seemed to have perfected the rigging technique. The turnout had taken about forty seconds and once away the Pump seemed much faster and smoother than the AFS green goddesses to which I was accustomed. The 'do-dah, do-dah' of the fire engine's two tone warning horns added a heightened note to this first emergency dash as a professional.

But this first callout to the house fire was a complete anticlimax. Within a minute of our noisy arrival at the house concerned, and after a very quick reconnaissance, it transpired that the alarm had been raised by young mother who had left a chip pan on her cooker. She had then had her attention distracted by her children and the chip pan had ignited. Fortuitously, she had not panicked but simply turned the cooker off and closed the kitchen door before summoning us. All that was needed was for the still flaming chip pan to be extinguished and removed to open air.

Had she attempted to move the burning pan a tragedy may have ensued, as pan and contents could have spilt and set fire to the contents of the kitchen and caused severe burns or worse to her, not to mention her two toddlers. There remained some clearing up and ventilation of the smoke filled kitchen whilst an ambulance crew comforted the shocked and shaking mother. She was full of apology for calling us out. Not that I minded – the more '999' calls the better!

Our Sub Officer must have sensed my disappointment that this, my first callout, had not been a dramatic working incident for before we left the scene and headed back to Old Town, he quietly called me over to the front of the fire engine.

'Now I understand you can't wait to get plenty of fire experience and all the excitement which goes with that, but remember one thing.' He paused to ensure that none of the rest of the crew were within earshot, and then continued, 'Every time we turn out to a 'shout' someone, somewhere, is in trouble or in dire peril. Don't forget that fact!'

These were very wise words as I was to discover before very long and over the next few tours of duty, both day and night, I tried to temper my enthusiasm and the adrenalin flow that came with each turnout. Over these early weeks there were small fires in a rubbish chute in a block of flats, and in a car engine compartment, some flooding incidents during a very wet and stormy night, and two instances of persons being stuck in a lift which failed between floors in Croydon's commercial centre.

About a month after I became a 'red rider', there was my first witness to real personal suffering. My watch had responded during the early evening to a '999' call to a 'bedroom on fire' in a pleasant residential area of South Croydon and sure enough, as we arrived at the semi-detached house, there was fairly thick smoke wafting out of an upstairs window.

A mattress and bedding was burning pretty fiercely and needed the efforts of a three man breathing apparatus crew and hosereel to penetrate the smoke, in order to damp the fire down and then bundle the smouldering mattress and bedding out of the window into the front garden, where it was finally extinguished. The cause of the fire was not an unusual one. One of the two elderly occupants of the house, a man and his wife, had apparantly unwittingly plugged in the electric blanket whilst using other electrical equipment during the morning. Thus the blanket had got progressively hotter and hotter during the day until it had spontaneously ignited.

Fortunately they had been alerted to their predicament whilst watching television downstairs, but in their distress the husband had tried to beat the developing fire out with a towel and only succeeded into sustaining some serious burns. My role at this incident was to care for him whilst awaiting an ambulance and although my recruit training had included a first aid qualification, I had not expected so early on in my career to be dealing with a casualty who was both coughing badly from smoke inhalation and had skin hanging down in strips from his forearms. Both he and his wife survived their ordeal which served to give me a little more experience with injured fire victims. It quickly became clear that the most important thing was to make your personal assurances to shocked casualties that 'all would be well' sound convincing, even if the injuries you were treating looked horrendous.

It was a full six months after I had completed my basic recruits training course and started operational duties at Croydon fire station before I was personally involved in a fire death, or in fireman's parlance, a 'stiff'.

The '999' call was to a house in a street just off London Road, West Croydon, around midday one cold November day. This area was a rundown tenement district where any fire call was potentially serious. The call out slip from the fire station teleprinter also said 'persons reported', indicating that the caller had stated that there were people trapped in the burning building.

I was one of the crew of the second of two fire engines – Pump Escape and Pump – that responded and we tore through the midday traffic, horns blaring out a stark note of warning. My seat in the back of the fire engine gave me a good view ahead over the driver's shoulder. As he swung the Pump into the street of the call, there beyond the Pump Escape ahead was an ominous pall of black smoke. A small crowd had already gathered outside the terrace house and as the two fire engines screeched to a halt, it was clear that there was a very severe fire in the downstairs front room. Upstairs, a black woman was crying from a window out of which thick smoke was pouring.

With our adrenalin flowing, we firefighters flew into action directed by our Station Officer. As the 50 foot wheeled escape ladder crunched down onto the road surface, three firemen turned it and then began extending it towards the frenetic form at the window above. One of the crew shouted out:

'Don't jump, do you hear? Hang on, we're almost there. We'll get you, hang on!'

Suddenly, the woman stopped screaming and yelled out:

'My kids are inside still – two kids. Oh, God!' and resorted to a high pitched wailing scream again.

Lockers flew open on the fire engines, and hose lines were being pulled out to knock down the worst of the angry flame now bursting out of the downstairs windows and threatening the rescue attempt above. I had been instructed to assist with taking a water jet in through the front door to extinguish the ground floor fire to allow a full search of the rest of the house for the missing children.

As the hose line hissed into life, I could see that the woman at the window had her arms appealingly outstretched like the a puppet in a Punch and Judy show. The escape ladder crew had almost got her.

Beneath this drama, my crew was now pulling the water jet through the front door and into the hallway and the swirling smoke inside. At this stage, only a fine water spray was turned on to keep us from scorching in the intense heat. Only feet inside the hall, the temperature was already burning my ears and face despite being crouched low.

By now, Leading Fireman Dave Trimble had found the door to the room on fire, and as he eased it ajar, he simultaeneously opened up with the powerful firefighting jet. For a split second, orange flame licked over our heads before we became completely enveloped in smoke, steam and flying sparks. I reached out and grasped the tunic of the fireman huddled close by me as if to seek some reassurance. It was impossible to do other than grunt, and he patted me on the back as we manhandled the heavy and throbbing hose line forward.

Then, just when my lungs felt they would burst, two breathing apparatus clad firemen relieved us and were then able to take the jet right into the depths of the room. Other crews with breathing sets swept past us up the stairs in their search for the youngsters. My colleague and I staggered out into the lovely fresh air of the street, only to find that the woman had been rescued down the escape ladder and was in a state of shock lying on the pavement awaiting removal to hospital. I went to assist the firemen who was already tending her and took my damp tunic off to drape over her sobbing and prostrate form.

Just then there was a muffled cry from within the house. 'We've got one, clear the stairs!' a voice called out.

Seconds later, a burly fireman in a breathing set emerged from the inner gloom carrying a small limp form in his arms. He laid the child down and tugging his facemask off, started mouth to mouth resuscitation on the lifeless form. But the fellow was clearly exhausted and drained by his rescue efforts in the torrid heat and I quickly took over from him. The kid was frothing at the mouth and nose and its whole body and the blackened clothes were still very warm. As I worked on, how desperate I was to see those little eyes flicker into life.

The child's mother, only some feet away, now started to scream out again and there were also some cries of anguish from the little crowd opposite. There were now more noises and cries in the background and as my resuscitation effort was handed over to an ambulance crew, I realised that the second youngster had been located and brought out. He, like the first, had been found under an upstairs bed, seeking refuge from the dense smoke and heat funnelling up from below.

Because of the number of casualties, several firefighters were assisting the crews of the two ambulances at the scene to get the mother and two children away to hospital. I travelled in the first vehicle with the two kids who each looked about four years old and helping with resuscitation was not easy, as the ambulance swayed through the traffic lights with its siren going.

Once at nearby Mayday Hospital the casualty staff took over and quickly dashed the fire victims inside, leaving Dave Trimble and myself standing in the clean corridor close to the casualty cubicles in our wet and grimy uniforms which now stank of smoke.

As we sat down to wait for some transport back to Croydon fire station, neither of us spoke. Dave like me had a young daughter, and he was probably thinking as I was. During my recruits course I had heard lurid tales of adult 'stiffs' and their gruesome recovery, but the experience of the last thirty minutes was not at all what I had been prepared for.

Then I suddenly became aware that the casualty sister was standing there. Again neither Dave nor I said anything as she gently shook her head at us both.

'I am so very sorry,' she said quietly. 'You must have done all you could.'

There was an unfamiliar sensation of loss deep inside as I recalled the training school adage that firemen must quickly learn to stand apart from the awful scenes of human tragedy and suffering that is so much part of their work. As we both walked out of the casualty entrance into the cool misty afternoon air to get into the now waiting staff car, I thought of the two little lives that had not long been taken. For the very first time, the real life and death nature of the proud profession I had not long joined, took on a new meaning.

Night shifts always seemed to add a special dimension to being a firefighter, especially once dusk had fallen. Indeed, I came to prefer the anticipation of what drama the night hours might bring. It was also on night duty that the cameraderie and team spirit of the watch shone through, be it through the help given to me in my probationary work by those senior to me undertaking their various promotion examinations, or through the banter and lampoonery that took place, especially during the 'stand down' periods after the evening drill session or technical lectures were over. Nobody on the watch seemed to take life too seriously and there was a great readiness to smile over the most trivial issue.

Nightime also brought more than its fair share of tragedies for firemen to sort out. Attendance at my first road accident fatality came following a 'shout' to a 'road traffic accident – persons trapped' at a notorious set of cross roads on Mitcham Common at about 0230 hours one chilly early springtime morning.

Both the Pump, which I was riding, and the Emergency Tender, were sent and the dash through the near deserted streets soon brought us upon the crash scene which at first sight looked like a breakers yard. Two cars had apparently collided at speed at right angles to each other on the traffic light intersection.

One vehicle, a white Austin 1100, was upturned on its roof with its front well stoved in and one wing torn right off. The other car was quite unrecognisable. For the sheer force of the collision had cut it in two main pieces, with many components being torn from the chassis and flung around the area of the road junction. Over a distance of some twenty yards or so were two wheels, a door, the entire rear axle assembly, and its bonnet.

As my colleagues and I ran towards the wreckage, our boots crunching on the glass strewn around, there was a lone policeman bending down over a huddled form in the road. He was shouting and pointing towards the upturned Austin. By the light of our torches we could see that there was a human form inside with feet towards us. One leg seemed to be twisted around at an awkward angle and there was no obvious movement from the casualty.

Our Sub Officer wriggled his shoulders and arms through the door space as the ET crew close by laid out the metal cutting equipment, first aid kits and blankets. Two firemen of the Pump crew quickly laid down a foam covering all around the Austin which was fast dripping petrol from its ruptured fuel tank. In the distance we could hear the welcome sound of approaching ambulances.

'One in here,' said the Sub back over his shoulder to me. 'Not badly trapped but dead, I'm pretty sure. Get the ambulance crew over here!'

As he spoke, I noticed that he had blood on both his gloved hands.

Two ambulances had now arrived and in one was a hospital casualty doctor. They quickly divided their attention between the Austin and the two people, a man and woman, both still lying unconcious in the road and presumably the driver and passenger of the second vehicle, which had literally disintegrated in the crash.

Helped by the Sub Officer and myself, the young doctor climbed into the Austin. There seemed to be a very long pause before he eased himself back out and shook his head. The doctor too now had blood stains on his reflective jerkin as well as some oil smears.

'He's gone!' he said quietly and ran off towards the other casualties being tended by the ambulance crews and several other firemen.

The area around the accident site was now being flood-lit by the Emergency Tender crew as other firefighters and I were directed to search the surrounding area of the commonland on all sides of the junction. The aim was to check for any stunned and walking wounded casualties who might have simply have wandered off into the night, or worse, those who had been thrown out of either car by the centrifugal forces unleashed at that awful moment of impact.

In the event, and after a careful examination of all the nearby areas of long grass, no further casualties were found. The sad tally of this one accident was three dead – although there were resuscitation attempts on one of those lying in the road, it was to no avail. The second person, the female, had little visible external injuries but remained lifeless.

There remained the task of releasing the body of the driver of the Austin once the police photographer had completed his task. This necessitated cutting away part of the side of the car to get at him. Then, as we eased the poor fellow out of his metal tomb and onto a stretcher, it was evident that the youthful driver had a massive head wound. Rather oddly, he was rather roughly dressed yet wore an expensive pair of leather shoes. As I leant over and covered his body with a blanket, there was an unmistakeable whiff of alcohol in the night air.

As the three bodies were placed in the ambulances and driven off to the mortuary, we handed over to the many police officers now at the scene and turned our attention to making up all the rescue equipment which had been in use or laid out. I realised that to work amid such carnage was going to be a regular experience for me in the years ahead.

And whilst this particular tragic incident was bad enough to have to deal with, I was yet to discover that the worst type of road crash was where badly injured, yet conscious, casualties were trapped in the compacted wreckage of vehicles from where they continually cried out for help throughout the rescue efforts of firefighters.

This sort of high drama was still to come.

4
High Drama

It did not take me long to realise that only a fairly small part of a firefighter's on duty time was spent dealing with '999' calls. In my first few tours of duty at Croydon, both day and night shifts, my watch was called to extinguish fires in a car, an overheated washing machine in a launderette, and to sort out a long neglected chimney from which we extracted twelve bucketfuls of smouldering soot. There was also a call to six people and two children stuck in a department store lift which had malfunctioned between floors.

However, each of these minor incidents took little time to bring under control before we returned to Old Town to prepare for the next 'shout'. And prepare we did. Most of the duty hours were spent in relentless practical drills using pumps, escape and other ladders, hose, breathing apparatus and all the plethora of fire and rescue equipment carried on the fire engines. The drills were designed to test our abilities to work both as a team and as individuals, in confined and awkward positions, both day and night in all weathers.

These outside drills were backed up by indoor technical lectures and 'situation' sessions where the watch officers would suggest a particular fire or accident scenario, usually with a couple of complications thrown in. These could be a total lack of mains firefighting water, or a traffic jam that prevented our fire engines from getting anywhere close to a fire where ladders were clearly needed. Once a situation had been set, we would then collectively describe the particular way we would deal with a given emergency. It was all breathtaking stuff, especially as at any time the turnout bells could clang throughout the fire station and within minutes, there facing us would be a situation where a person's life or death would literally be in our hands.

In addition to all this preparation, there were regular fitness training periods, not only of the old fashioned PT variety but utilising team games such as volleyball. Everyone took part, including the watch officers and throughout these sometimes boisterous sessions the cameraderie and espirit-de-corps was much in evidence.

But all this was rather offset by the cleaning work which then formed part of a firefighter's lot. There were the lavatories and shower blocks, and the floors of the kitchen and living accomodation, as well as the dormitories to keep clean. In addition, twice a week there was a scrub and wash out of the huge six bay engine house and its tiled floors. Inevitably, the washing out was done with a high pressure fire hose and regularly turned into a bit of a water carnival in which the other two probationers and I usually ended up fairly wet!

Several years later, as part of a national agreement, this work was given over to contractors in order to free fire crews to undertake more fire prevention and safety visits in the community. This was a positive step forward in utilising the proper skills of firefighters in this way, but it is fair to say that up and down the land, fire stations ceased to be as absolutely spotless and shiny as they had been all those previous years.

Just occasionally, there did occur a largish fire in the Croydon area which took a concerted effort and several hours to control. Then there would be a prolonged period, often extending well into a whole day or night shift, when firefighters would go on to carry out salvage work and damping down duties. Several times during my early months, I reported for duty to find that my watch was detailed to relieve the off-going crews who were still damping down at the scene of a medium sized fire which had occured some hours earlier. As my crew arrived at the still smoking and steaming scene, my envy at those colleagues on the duty watch who had been part of the excitement as they first arrived at the conflagration must have been obvious to all around. But that is not to say that these early stages of my career where not without moments of sudden and high drama.

Midway through a blustery and windy October morning, came a '999' call to the shopping area of London Road, Thornton Heath, where a large rooftop television aerial which had been loosened in the high wind was now threatening to crash down onto the pavement area below.

On this particular shift, I was riding as the fourth man of the Turntable Ladder (TL) crew and recalling my hectic ride at Southwark training school, high up at 100 feet on a TL, there was a real expectancy of some action. Little could I foresee what was to come.

After the noisy dash through the rainswept traffic, the twelve ton fire engine, at twenty eight feet long one of the largest in fire service use, drew up outside the shops in London Road. The Croydon TL was one of eighteen such appliances located strategically across Greater London. It did, therefore, occasionally travel off its home ground when a high rise capability was urgently needed, as in this case.

George, our Leading Fireman in charge of the TL quickly conferred with his opposite number of the Thornton Heath Pump and Malcolm, the TL driver/operator, along with a police constable all looked skywards up to the offending aerial as it drooped dangerously over the pavement. As far as we could see through the driving rain, the aerial appeared to be mounted on the edge of the roof of the three floors of residential flats above the shops. Fortunately, the PC and the Thornton Heath fire crew had already cordoned off the pavement area below as quite a sizeable crowd had already gathered to watch the firefighters deal with the situation.

After a rapid briefing by George, Malcolm gently drove the TL up onto the wide pavement close to the shopfronts, and carefully positioned the fire engine. He then put the four TL jacks down, one on each side of the back axle. These provided a firm base during the operation of the ladder. Then sitting at the ladder controls, Malcolm quickly elevated the ladder sections ready to shoot the other member of the TL crew, Ray, up to about 90 feet close by the drooping aerial.

I was instructed to stay close to Malcolm at the TL controls and be ready to assist as directed. Leading Fireman George positioned himself a little distance away so as to oversee the operation, whilst Ray had now got a long line around him, bandolier fashion. He then climbed up onto the ladder, and quickly hooked himself on.

Malcolm then started to shoot Ray up at an angle of some 65 degrees towards the aerial, and the metal ladder sections clattered as they extended higher and higher. I stood on the TL chassis just behind Malcolm at the controls and as we both looked up at the ever diminishing figure of Ray, the rain poured down our necks. As the TL's diesel engine note rose in response to the ladder operation, I could feel the whole chassis tremble.

'Ray,' called out Malcolm over the TL intercom system, 'I'm going to stop at about 80 feet and let you guide me in. I shall train slightly left when you're ready. You sing out when you're close enough to get the line round it.'

As he spoke there was a strong and prolonged gust of wind which blew the rain sideways across us and the TL chassis actually seemed to be flexing under our feet.

'OK, and understood' responded Ray over the system speaker on the control console. 'Come very slightly left, Malc, and gently does it. It bloody hairy up here already!'

Malcolm then operated the control lever which slowly turned the whole ladder around the turntable. I took another upwards glance into the windblown rain and spray at the four tons of ladder pointing skywards and decided that Ray could have this particular moment of uncomfortable glory up on his perch on high.

Then, just as he was close enough to reach out and grab the aerial, horror of horrors! Another sudden and sustained blast of wind sent a shudder through the TL's chassis which immediately translated its normal flexing motion into a slight rocking motion, sideways across the fire engine. This in turn was transmitted right up the 80 feet of extended ladder sections to Ray at the top. The whole apparatus then started to tilt one way away from the frontage of the flats, then back towards them.

With the wind roaring past us, Malcolm was faced with a impossible decision – to house the ladder and bring Ray down, which would take some thirty seconds or so, or to get Ray to unhook and descend through the wind and rain. Either way was going to be risky but he lost no time.

'Ray, get the hell down from up there, do you hear?' shouted Malcolm into the intercom. 'I'm going to try and rest the ladder top onto the roof.'

The console speaker seemed to explode in immediate response.

'Jesus Christ! Keep it still. I'm coming down!' cried Ray so loud that all around the TL could hear.

Seeing what was happening to the tilting ladder from his vantage point close by, George was also quick to act as he shouted out to the Thornton Heath fire crew.

'All of you, get your weight up on the chassis and bloody quick!'

As the six firefighters leapt up onto the now crowded flat area around the TL control console, I noticed that the two appliance jacks on the nearside where about a foot clear of the pavement.

'More of you, come on, up on the chassis,' appealed George to the spectating crowd behind the cordon some fifty yards away.

The TL had now taken on a seemingly permanent list, fortunately in towards the shops and flats above and George, himself an experienced TL operator, knew it was imperative to get some more weight exerting down to counteract the wind acting upon the 80 feet of ladder above.

'That's it,' he cried out to the six or so men who

climbed up onto the TL chassis. 'More of you, come on, bear down on the sides,' and uncerimoniously pushed the PC into the assisting group of civilians. 'Bear down, push down,' shouted George into the wind and rain. 'Hold it down!'

Malcolm meanwhile was watching Ray's descent, for once the firefighter up aloft had unhooked and started to come down, the two could no longer converse over the intercom.

'Come on old son,' muttered Malcolm, 'come on down!'

But Ray needed no further bidding to get down from his perilous position. He was coming down the TL like an animated monkey, as fast as a recruit at ladder drill at Southwark, except that the TL ladder was still leaning over in towards the roof of the building as if held in freeze frame. As the wind buffetted us, I had an awful feeling that the TL was gathering itself to suddenly crash right over.

At the precise moment Ray reached the bottom of the ladder and jumped down onto the pavement, the tilting mass of the ladder above appeared to be responding to the combined leverage forces being applied below. Very slowly, almost imperceptibly, the four tons of ladder pointing skywards started to come back into the vertical position.

Now that Ray was safely on the ground, Malcolm began to house the ladder sections, but I could see that the TL was not responding to its controls. Ray stood close by looking up. He had taken his helmet off to mop the rain off his face and his dark hair was being blown around in the wind.

'What bloody well happened there?' he exclaimed, breathlessly. 'I really thought I was going over!'

Before anyone could answer him, the TL suddenly righted itself and came back into the fully vertical plane as its nearside jacks crunched down onto the pavement. All eyes were now looking up as the ladder sections, still extended to about 80 feet, momentarily seemed to sway over in the opposite direction as the reactionary forces played themselves out. The top of the ladder was visibly shaking several feet from side to side but as suddenly as it had keeled over, the TL now appeared to be stable.

Malcolm was still at the controls and managed to get some response. He eased the ladder head down on to a coping stone at the edge of the roof of the building, thus ensuring the stability of the fire engine and there was a audible sigh from all of us, both firefighters and members of the public who were gathered around the base of the TL as the tension was broken. The whole episode had only lasted about a minute or so but it seemed like an age, especially to Ray. Rain still lashed down and the wind blew but we cared not, for a potential tragedy had been averted.

As if to remind us all of the cause of the original '999' call, there was an unexpected crash followed by a shower of brickwork and guttering as the television aerial fell into the cordoned area. Fortunately, nobody was struck by the flying debris.

The immobilised TL, which was only some six years old, was eventually recovered by fire service engineers some hours later when the strong winds had subsided somewhat. There was a subsequent inquiry which found that whilst certain special procedures for operating a TL in windy conditions had been complied with, these arrangements clearly needed to be broadened to take account of stronger gusts. As a result, regular and precise meteriological wind forecasts were issued to TL fire stations which then precluded their use above a certain height limit.

After this dramatic incident I tried hard to retain faith in the safety and strength of these massive fire engines. It also left me with a greater awareness and respect of the difficulties that Mother Nature could create for firefighters and Ray, of course, had very good reason to remember the call to London Road more than most.

Soon after this dramatic incident, I was successful in

getting a transfer from Croydon to the inner London area. The coming of the Greater London Council in 1965 had created a enlarged London Fire Brigade of some 124 fire stations into which went the old Middlesex, Croydon, East and West Ham brigades, along with some fire stations of Kent, Surrey, and Hertfordshire. With the inaugaration of one of the largest firefighting forces in the world came the opportunity to gain experience in the busiest operational districts of the capital.

My transfer took me to Chelsea fire station of the 'A' division of the London Fire Brigade – whose nine other fire stations protected an area which included Westminster, Soho, Bayswater, Mayfair, Euston, Kensington and Notting Hill. Chelsea fire station was listed as A27 and was located midway along the Kings Road, then the centre of the youth fashion world. This was also the time of the Beatles, flower power and the mini skirt, and to be a young firefighter amid all this cultural and cosmopolitan world was, to put it mildly, like being on the campus of the university of life.

The three watches – red, white and blue – totalled some 36 firefighters. Between them they manned the three fire engines based at Chelsea, – Pump Escape, Pump and Hose Layer (HL). This latter fire engine was only infrequently used at major fires where additional large scale firefighting water supplies from trunk mains were needed. The HL (or 'Layer' as it was known) carried about ½ a mile of large diameter hose which was laid out over the tailboard whilst the HL moved along at about 20 mph.

One novelty of the HL, of which there were six in London, was that it carried a cycle on board. Once the 'Layer' had laid out all its hose and reached its objective, (usually a Pump near the scene of the fire), the cycle enabled a member of the HL crew to get quickly back to the trunk main into which the HL had tapped. There the hydrant valve would be turned on after which the firefighter would pedal frantically back over the ½ mile to rejoin the rest of the crew. These cycles were, of course, painted fire engine red and were even allocated a vehicle fleet number!

But one incident which indirectly involved Chelsea's HL served to once again graphically highlight the dangers of firefighting. It all started with the attendance of the HL at a big night time fire – needing the combined efforts of about 100 firemen and twenty pumps – at a plastics factory at Brentford, in West London. The 'Layer' was called out at about 0600 hours and as Tony, the driver, headed the fire engine westward down Cromwell Road, we could already see the orange glow lighting up the night sky.

At that time of the early morning, it only took us about ten minutes to reach the scene where I reported the HL in attendance at the Control Unit. By then, the fire glow above the factory about 100 yards down the street was dying down although the pungent toxic smoke from the burning plastics was swirling everywhere. After the Control Unit staff had spoken briefly to the fire commander via personal radio, I was told that the Chelsea 'Layer' was not needed this time as the fire was coming under control and there were no particular water shortages.

Tony and I climbed back on board the HL, extracted ourselves from the melee of firefighters, hose lines and parked fire pumps, slightly thankful that we had not been asked to get the 'Layer' to work. Replacing and restowing the HL with clean and dry hose could be a backbreaking three hours work.

We eventually got going and headed off back to Chelsea at a far more sedate pace than we had arrived. Dawn was breaking and the early morning commuter and commercial traffic into the capital was already beginning to build up. It must have been around 0800 hours as we crawled up to the traffic lights at the very busy junction of Battersea Bridge and Chelsea Embankment, when Tony first spotted a motorcyclist pushing his mount about fifty yards or so ahead of us in the traffic stream. The motorbike was wobbling somewhat and appeared to have a puncture.

'That's Colin Comber of the Red Watch,' said Tony, 'Let's see if he wants some help'.

We soon overhauled the motorcyclist and he looked up at us as the towering fire engine slowly came alongside. His eyes suddenly lit up and he gave us a beaming smile.

'Well blow me!' he exclaimed. 'Am I pleased to see you. I've pushed this damn thing from the other side of Battersea Bridge and its getting bloody heavy! Any chance of a lift? Otherwise I'm going to be late for parade'.

It was, of course, completely against all Brigade instructions but in no time at all, Colin and I had lifted the motorcycle up into the rear of the HL and secured it carefully amid all the rows of flaked hose. He was in his early forties, of stocky build with a rosy complexion, and as he removed his crash helmet he displayed a sweaty brow and dark tousled hair that was thinning on top.

As we both climbed up into the crew cab of the HL, Colin's mind turned to enquire where we had been.

'I hope you White Watch buggers haven't used any hose on the Layer!' he said, as Tony moved the fire engine off back into the impatient traffic queues ahead.

'We've been very quiet lately on Red Watch,' he continued with a hint of a smile. 'Except that is for clearing up after all the working jobs that the White and Blue seem to go to just before change of watch!'

As I had not long arrived at Chelsea fire station, it was taking me a little time to get to know all the two dozen or so firemen on the other two watches, especially with the complications of the shift duty patterns.

Thus this was the first and last time that I properly met Fireman Colin Comber of the Red Watch, attached to Chelsea fire station, London Fire Brigade. For less than a month later, he was killed in action at a fire.

Both Pump Escape and Pump crewed by the Red Watch had responded to a midnight fire call which took them to a smoke filled restaurant in Kings Road, only half a mile or so from Chelsea fire station. Colin Comber along with Fireman Brian Hutchins, both in breathing apparatus, had taken a hose line into the thick black smoke at ground floor level to try to locate the seat of the fire. As they both moved into the hot swirling darkness, the two firefighters were suddenly engulfed in an explosive flashover – a rolling and ferocious ball of flame which consumed everything in its path.

The sheer force of the fiery explosion blew out the restaurant windows and both Colin and Brian were fatally burnt. Despite being taken immediately to a specialist burns unit, they both died a most painful death within an hour or so of each other, some 48 hours after the fire.

My first awareness of the fire and its casualties came as I listened to my car radio, en route for a White Watch day duty at Chelsea the morning after the tragedy. At that early stage, no names of the firemen involved had been given out to the media.

Only when I turned into the station drill yard, parked my car and walked over to one of the fire engine bays, did the enormity of the situation become clear. For there being laid out for official photographs on clean plastic salvage sheets were the scorched remains of two sets of uniform. Both fire tunics were almost in fragmented pieces. One of the two blackened fire helmets was also badly mishapen yet the name of its wearer – 'C. Comber A27 Chelsea' – was just discernible inside. My mind went immediately back to the lift on the Hose Layer which Tony and I had been able to offer Colin a short while back.

After all the full and moving panoply of a brigade funeral for both firemen, came fresh calls for better protective firefighting uniforms. For to be caught in a flashover – caused when a build up of unburnt gases suddenly ignite – has long been the worst fear of all firefighters. Although newer fire resistant materials, allied to improved uniform design were not forthcoming for several more years, the ultimate danger of the profession could not have been more vividly and horrifyingly illustrated.

Another particularly dramatic and, sadly, fatal fire of

this busy operational period in London's 'A' Division gave me some rather special excitement. For it was the one of the few occasions when I actually climbed a hook ladder in a rescue attempt and got myself singed into the bargain.

The '999' call was answered one early November evening by Manchester Square fire station, just off Oxford Street, to where I had been posted from Chelsea as part of my promotion path. Apart from the address on the teleprinter call-out slip from London Fire Brigade Control which said 'Crawford Street, W1', the only other information given by the caller was 'rubbish bins on fire'.

Only one fire engine and crew were normally sent to deal with such minor fires. However, as we turned into Crawford Street, which was only about one minute's running time from Manchester Square fire station, it was very evident that the three of us forming the crew – Station Officer, driver and myself – had got a fire situation of heroic proportions on our hands. For instead of several smouldering rubbish bins awaiting us, there ahead about halfway down Crawford Street and its tenement buildings, was a deep orange fire glow. As we neared the scene, I could see thick black smoke pouring from the upper windows of the four storey building and an intensely fierce fire in the street entrance doorway which was funnelling up the staircase. Quite a sizeable crowd had already gathered to watch the unfolding drama.

As we pulled up close to the burning tenement building, several bystanders shouted out.

'There's two people up there. Both elderly! Get them out!'

'On the third floor – be quick!'

But we three firefighters had a near impossible task. The Station Officer was immediately calling for assistance over the radio, whilst our driver had already engaged the water pump and was frantically running out a hose line from the fire engine lockers.

Fire was now roaring out of the street doorway with a ferocity I had not yet experienced and the radiated heat rippled over us in waves. I grabbed a hook ladder off the Pump, pulled the hook out and thrust the ladder up to the first floor windows as far to one side from the flames as I could get. With some difficulty on the swaying ladder, I got up to the first floor window ledge and putting one arm through a cast iron guard rail, was able to pitch the ladder up again to the window above me on the second floor.

But as I crept, monkey like ever higher, I knew that without some help my lone rescue attempt was doomed. As I came up to the third floor window it was already well blackened by the fire and heat inside the room. Worse still was the thick acrid smoke being forced out under pressure all around the window frame, showing that the room was near to 'flashover'. Our driver below had now got a single jet of water to work, and in between trying to keep the fire down in the ground floor staircase area, he turned its cooling stream upwards to where I was in some danger of being roasted three floors up the face of the tenements. As he did so, the water turned to steam as it hit the hot brickwork alongside me.

Indeed, the scorching heat from both within and below me was getting unbearable and my ladder felt precarious and unstable. There was no iron rail around the third floor window to hold on to, and the hook of the ladder was only resting on the stone cill of the window opening. I feared that if the glass blew out, I could be blown off my high perch. It was now sadly clear that I could not get into the building at this level. Small burning fragments were also beginning to drop from above.

By the time I got back down to street level, firefighting was well under way. Three other fire engines were now at the scene and more could be heard approaching noisily in the distance. Teams of firemen in breathing apparatus were working hose jets up the staircase, knocking down the fire as they went and two 50 foot wheeled escape ladders were being pitched into the face of the building.

It was only when my feet touched the wet and steaming

pavement that I noticed a burning sensation on the backs of both hands as well as my forehead. There was also blood dripping from several small cuts as an ambulance crew came to my aid. By then, the fire crews inside had forced their way up to the second floor. There inside the front room to which I had been so close, they found the two badly charred bodies, amid the steamy heat and humidity of the burnt-out flat.

Ten minutes later, two other firefighters and I were in the casualty department of nearby St. Mary's Hospital nursing our minor injuries and all wishing we could have done more to save the lives of the perished couple.

After the usual forensic examination of the fire scene, the cause was returned as arson. Whoever had perpetrated this crime had poured a flammable substance, believed to be petrol, over the contents of a number of overflowing rubbish bins piled up inside the entrance way to flats above. The rapid upward spread of fire had simply trapped the two victims without any other means of escape.

Subsequent inquiries also established that there had been a fatal delay of some minutes before the fire brigade had been called. Neighbours and onlookers had all assumed that 'someone else' had rung '999'. Sadly for several minutes no one did, allowing the initial small fire to quickly grow up the staircase and into the flat above before the first firefighters arrived on the scene.

There was even some criticism of the brigade at the coroner's inquest into the fire, in that several witnesses said it had taken some time before the first jet of water was got to bear on the fire. These unfair comments rather hurt all those of us involved in this tragic incident. With only three on the crew, there was obviously a limit to what we could do. In further evidence, it then became obvious that the closest fire hydrant – only thirty yards away – had been obscured by the crowd of onlookers standing right on top of it!

However, the Coroner praised all those firemen

involved for their efforts in trying to save the elderly couple, but for many weeks after I could not help feeling that had there been a more prompt '999' fire call to Crawford Street on that fateful evening, then our rescue efforts might just have made the difference between life and death.

London Turnout

We're out and the Pump Escape's flying,
It's a shout to a fire in a house,
In a district where 'Persons reported',
Is more common these days than a mouse.

Tom Arnold our driver is swearing,
'Curse the traffic, its always at peaks,'
Some eight tons of hope he is weaving,
Any hole we can get through he seeks.

Two-tone horns are blasting we're coming,
The Guv'nor is bashing the bell.
Lord God, though we know well our duty,
Give your aid and we'll save them from hell.

Policemen are running before us,
They're determined to break up a jam,
Return our salute as we pass them,
For they know we do well when we can.

Charles Clisby, Divisional Officer, London Fire Brigade.

5
Kids will be Kids

Firefighters in both city and rural brigades would surely agree that children seem to have little difficulty in challenging the fire service with a wide range and variety of rescue situations. And in many such emergencies, even the most simple and innocent playtime object can be transformed into a perilous device, as some of my own experiences have shown.

Take a simple galvanised mop bucket, for instance. Who would ever imagine that the combination of such an everyday household article and a young toddler could be the cause of a most unusual call for help?

It all happened one spring morning in Islington, North London, when a three year old boy called Johnny was at play in the garden of his terraced home when he became bored with his toys and in exploring around, came across his mother's mop bucket. After a while, he decided to climb into it; after all it was just the right size for him. But as he wriggled in and sat down with his little knees drawn up tightly under his chin, it was rather uncomfortable. Johnny then pushed his knees under the half-lip mop squeezer which covered half of the top of the bucket only to find that he was now wedged very fast. It was at this stage he yelled out for his mum.

Fortunately, Johnny's mother was close by and quickly realised her son's predicament and rang '999'. By the time that my crew arrived from Islington fire station, the boy was in tears and being comforted by his mum, who by this time was also rather upset.

It was obvious from the start that we could not easily use any form of metal cutters on the bucket. A more subtle approach was needed but first it was necessary to stop Johnny from crying and try and settle him down a little. This was achieved by getting him to put on my fire helmet, which he readily did and immediately this ploy brought a smile to his face, even if the oversize headgear flopped about on his dark curly hair. Because of this, Johnny had to hold on the outer edges of the fire helmet which was a good thing, as it served to keep his arms up enabling us to determine the task ahead.

After a little deliberation, I asked the boy's mother if we could have some butter. Without asking any questions, she shot inside to her kitchen and was quickly back with two packs.

'These are too hard, love,' I said. 'Can you warm them up a bit, even to it being soft and runny?'

Again, she took off inside her kitchen close by. Whilst she was indoors complying with my request, my crew of four firemen sat on the grass in the bright sunshine in a circle around Johnny as they kept him smiling and laughing with silly faces, and sundry promises to let him go and sit in our fire engine after his ordeal was over. I too, smiled and looked on from the kitchen door at these hardened men of action and the captive boy in the bucket, all the time hoping that this was not going to be a protracted and difficult rescue.

After a minute or so, Johnny's mum emerged with a saucepan full of semi-liquid butter. After telling the boy what we were going to do, I very carefully started to spread the golden mixture around his midriff and around the lip of the bucket. More of the liquid was poured around the same area in the hope that it would percolate down.

Then very, very gently, I started to try to lift Johnny, at the same time as the rest of the crew applied a slight turning motion to the bucket, first one way, and then the other. As soon as this twisting operation commenced the boy, still with my fire helmet on, actually started laughing quite loudly. This at least gave me the confidence to continue even if he still seemed firmly stuck.

We paused after several minutes to smear and pour

more of the butter around Johnny again and then resumed the twisting and gentle pulling. Just as I was beginning to envisage a cutting job on the offending bucket, suddenly there was upward movement and Johnny popped out just like a champagne cork. My four colleagues all cheered and I quickly passed the now-greasy youngster to his mother for a cuddle. He beamed at us from over her shoulder as he hugged her but then moved quickly to resume his two handed grip on my fire helmet.

The problem was then to retrieve the helmet without any tears. This was only achieved after we had promised Johnny one of his own, and had let him sit behind the wheel of Islington's shiny new Dennis Pump. This was much to the chagrin of the driver, who found that there was now butter smeared all over the wheel, gear shift and handbrake controls.

Later in the day whilst returning from some fire prevention inspections, we called back to see Johnny, who appeared to be none the worse for his adventure. There we presented the toddler with a plastic replica fire helmet of the sort sold at fire service charity events, and in our own way thus marked a rescue of a rather unusual nature.

And for several days afterwards, successive shift drivers of the Dennis Pump at Islington complained of the distinctly greasy feel of the fire engine controls, which only five of us knew had more than a little to do with a pound of best British butter.

Another instance where a quite innocent situation involving a child contrived to cause a fire service turnout, this time to the intense embarrassment of the parents concerned, started during the Whitsun school holidays and a day trip to London for Lisa and her parents. They started the day with the Changing of the Guard at Buckingham Palace outside where the drama took place.

Lisa and her Mum and Dad had arrived in good time and had secured a front row place up against the palace railings, from where to view the ceremony. As the crowd grew to its usual size of several hundred spectators, the band could be heard coming in the distance as the 1130 am time for the start of the guard changing approached.

By then, Lisa had got herself right up against the railings and found that she could just get her head through the uprights, which gave her a much better view of the palace forecourt and the scarlet tunics of the guardsmen lined up waiting the arrival of the approaching band. This was fine until Lisa wanted to talk to her parents close behind her, tried to pull her head out and quickly realised she was stuck fast in the Royal railings.

Now such a situation was not unknown to London firemen who, over the years, had developed a very simple expanding screw device which was able to push two adjacent railings apart just sufficient enough to ease a child's head out.

And so it was on this occasion. When Lisa's parents realised their daughter's plight they had summoned a nearby PC, who in turn radioed for the London Fire Brigade. Thus when a Pump and Emergency Tender and ten firemen arrived outside Buckingham Palace, the Changing of the Guard was well under way and although the two fire engines approached silently, Lisa's predicament was certainly causing a distraction to the main event.

However, in the twinkling of an eye, the fire crews used the railing expander to good effect and Lisa was soon able to pull her head out of the railings and be tearfully reunited with her embarrassed parents. They were both overwhelming in their thanks for the speedy response of the firefighters and as the band of the Welsh Guards played on, Lisa's parents led her away, no doubt towards a London attraction which did not have a set of railings around it!

Even a child's bicycle can cause problems for firemen from time to time, as one 12 year old boy in Regent's Park quickly found out. It was during the early summertime craze of 'BMX' bikes and some undoubted tomfoolery had led to him to crash and put his foot very forcibly through the spokes of the rear wheel. As he did so, the spokes acted like a vice upon the skin of his bare leg.

My crew arrived in Regent's Park at the same time as an ambulance and we eventually located the lad being tended by his mates close by the rear perimeter of the Zoological Gardens. It looked as if he had broken his leg in the crash and this needed to be splinted by the ambulance crew before we could cut the spokes away to allow for his careful removal. Despite his obvious pain, the boy was not at all pleased when he realised that we were taking our cutting equipment to his beloved and nearly new BMX bike.

'My Dad'll give me 'ell,' he cried as the air operated cutters snipped musically through about six spokes.

'Do you 'ave to do that, Mister?' he continued imploringly. 'He'll bloody kill me, he will. Honest!'

I felt the utmost compassion for the injured boy, but this was the only way to untangle him from his bike and get him off to hospital for the treatment he urgently needed. As the young casualty was put gently into the ambulance, I hoped his father would be kind to him in the knowledge that a few spokes were a small price to pay for the speedy extrication of his exuberant son.

But just now and again, came a '999' call to a serious emergency where a child's life and limbs were in perilous danger. Such turnouts would inevitably develop into a battle against the clock as the two following accounts show.

Lola, an attractive fair haired three year old, had not long arrived one morning at London's Euston railway station with her father. He placed the little girl in the seat section of a wheeled luggage trolley, turned his back for their cases and before he could say 'Little Bo Peep', Lola was protesting aloud that the tip of her right hand index finger was well and truly stuck in a tiny gap under the handle of the luggage trolley.

Lola's father quickly attempted to release the trapped finger, to no avail except for an increasing amount of vociferous yelling from his daughter. The finger stayed firmly jammed.

Father took stock of the trolley; it was similar to those found in supermarkets and constructed of a square section steel frame with wire mesh sides. The pushing handle also acted as a brake lever, for when it was pushed downwards it actuated brake pads on the trolley rear wheels through a series of rods concealed within the trolley frame.

By now, Lola's anguish had reached a pitch of sobbing and fright and her father paused no more. He hurriedly summoned a patrolling PC who quickly radioed for an ambulance. When this arrived some minutes later, its crew took one look at Lola's predicament and her swelling index finger and promptly carried Lola plus trolley accompanied by her father into the ambulance for the short journey to nearby University College Hospital.

There, Lola was gently unloaded from the ambulance and wheeled into the casualty department, where the duty doctor rapidly decided that this unusual extrication job was going to be a task for the London Fire Brigade.

Soon after the Pump Escape and Pump from Euston fire station, together with an Emergency Tender from Paddington, arrived. The Station Officer in charge quickly took stock of the situation and air-operated cutters were run into the casualty department. As the cutting saw was being prepared for use by firefighters in the cubicle where Lola was being comforted, the doctor administered a mild sedative injection to calm her and soothe her fears of what was to come.

It was at about this stage that I arrived on the scene as the duty senior officer. Throughout the next half-hour Lola yelled and cried pitifully despite the assurances of her father, myself and other firemen, not to mention the nursing staff. Lola's staccato cries echoed through the casualty cubicles and out into the main foyer of the hospital. There the long rows of seated patients awaiting the afternoon clinics looked concernedly towards the direction of the girl's cries. And the hurried activity of firemen carrying yet more cutting equipment into the casualty department from their fire engines outside, heightened the puzzlement of this plastered and bandaged audience as to just what was going on.

Inside the cubicle, the tears flowed as Lola's father knelt down on his knees alongside his daughter, one of his arms tightly around her, close and comforting. He too was looking pale and distraught; his upward glances asked us for her rapid and painless release. Lola's long fair hair had become tousled and was quite damp at the front where she had constantly rubbed her wet eyes with her one free hand.

'Daddy,' she implored. 'Daddy, Daddy!'

Once all the cutting equipment was laid out ready the majority of the crews adjourned out of sight around the corner, leaving several firefighters to start the cutting operation. When the doctor was confident that the sedative had taken, Lola's right arm was firmly supported and cutting of the trolley began. But despite plenty of reassurances as the saw blade was brought in as close as possible to the trolley handle near to Lola's jammed finger tip, she screamed and thrashed around in the trolley seat.

Worse was to follow. After only a few careful strokes of the saw, the Leading Fireman manipulating the rescue tool could see that this direct approach was not going to work. All the parts of the brake rod mechanism under the trolley handle were of hardened steel. Lola continued to kick out especially when the air-operated saw hissed each time it stopped, making it almost impossible to achieve an accurate and delicate approach to the cutting job in hand.

To further complicate the situation, after ten minutes or so the doctor called me over to one side and expressed his growing concern about the child's swelling index finger, and the clear need to extricate her as soon as possible if he was going to have any chance of saving the finger tip.

A further plan was then evolved. Lola would be

further sedated to a point where she would be very
drowsy. The entire corner unit of the trolley around her
would then be cut away. Fortunately, this structure
appeared to be of a softer steel although this plan would
still mean cutting through one hardened brake rod. The
little girl would then be taken down to the hospital
engineers' workshop close by with the corner piece still
on her finger. In the workshop, I hoped that we would
achieve her final release.

Poor Lola cried out continually as she was given more
injections whilst the fire crew waited impatiently for several minutes for the doctor to give us the 'go ahead'. The
girl's finger had been trapped for over half an hour and
it seemed an age before he nodded his approval for the
cutting to re-commence.

This time, the air saw cut rapidly into the trolley main
frame and soon parted the corner unit. However, the
brake rod took over five minutes to saw through, but once
this was done the entire corner piece was almost free.
Much of this sawing work went on only inches from
Lola's finger and to combat the heat generated by the
sawing, one fireman held a large syringe filled with cold
water with which he regularly anointed the trapped finger
and the surrounding metal area.

All this extensive work occupied another half hour or
so, by which time Lola's head rolled from side to side as
the drugs took full effect, although she never seemed to
go right into a deep sleep. Now and then she recovered
from her stupor to cry out again, whereupon a nurse read
aloud passages from a nursery rhyme book held open in
front of the trapped girl.

Eventually, the final saw cut through the main frame
was made and a very drowsy Lola was gently and carefully
lifted out of the trolley by her father. Alongside, a firefighter supported her right hand whilst another took the
full weight of the small metal corner assembly inside
which her finger tip was still jammed.

Once she had been carried down a nearby flight of

stairs and into the engineer's workshop, Lola was laid down upon clean bedding on the workbench. As her father reassured her again, a fresh set of cutting gear and tools was laid out ready all around, as we set off on the second part of the unusual rescue. The girl's right hand was again firmly held still whilst the metal assembly was clamped up tight in one of the engineers' bench vices.

An attempt was then made to drive a quarter inch steel jointing pin off its seating. This pin had been exposed by our earlier cutting work and it was now clear that Lola's finger tip was stuck under this pin. We had rigged up some portable floodlights in the workshop and in their harsh light, I could now see that the girl's finger tip was quite blue. I tried not to dwell on the implications of amputation.

With the rescue attempt now well into its second hour, the metal pin stubbornly refused to budge despite some determined effort with various tools bits. Only a very limited amount of pressure could be used but it was clear to us all that if this pin could be driven down just half an inch or so, Lola's finger tip would be free.

We then resorted to drilling out the upper end of the pin, but this was abandoned due to the proximity of the child's finger. Other firefighters then worked gently on the pin itself until they had made a saw cut deep enough to take a sharp chisel. Then using a specially adapted punch ground to shape at the scene, the critical pin was slowly tapped down out of its seating little by little, until suddenly Lola's hand was at last lifted free from the metal structure by the doctor.

She was then hurriedly carried away from the workshop back into the casualty department by the doctor with her father and several nurses in close pursuit. I glanced at my watch. For the first time in almost two hours we could relax and as the crews started to pick up all the host of rescue gear used in the operation, there were plenty of grins to be seen. But had we worked fast enough to save the finger tip? Glancing at the half-sawn unrecognisable metal structure still clamped in the vice and the offending pin inside the mass, it seemed incredible that such a small component could be the cause of such a trauma.

Then heading upstairs and turning into the casualty department, I saw through an open door the doctor sitting alongside Lola who was laid out on the bed in a small operating theatre. He now had a white mask over his face and was working on Lola's hand with some instruments. I could hear the girl was still crying despite the close attention of her father and two nurses.

Not wishing to intrude, I started to make my way out to the fire engines and my staff car in the street when the doctor stood up, and called me inside.

'She's going to be alright,' he said quietly as he pulled his mask down and revealed a broad grin.

Lola's sobbing had now ceased and all about seemed very silent except for the clank of instruments being put into trays nearby.

'Her finger tip is going to be OK,' the doctor continued. 'Thanks for all your skill and help. Your lads did a super job!'

I thanked him for all the hospital's effort and paused until the nurse had finished dressing Lola's finger. Then her father picked her off the bed and gave her an intense cuddle as she in turn clung to him with both arms tightly around his neck.

'Please thank your blokes,' was all he could manage to say to me before he choked on his words.

As he turned away still gently patting his daughter's back, her face came into full view over his shoulder. There upon Lola's pretty tear-stained face was the very first smile since our brief encounter began over two hours ago.

The second serious 'children' potential tragedy dealt with by Paddington firemen involved a struggle to free the arm of Salim, a young Pakistani boy, from inside a mincing machine in his mother's butchers shop. Salim had been playing near the mincing machine which was

operating, and in a fateful motion, he put his fingers into
the feeder funnel of the machine. In a split-second, the
boy's arm was drawn up into the machine until Salim's
little finger tips appeared at the outlet as with an awful
sound, the mincing machine suddenly stopped.

Very soon, three fire engines from Paddington fire
station, an ambulance and a police car arrived at the shop.
Although Salim was concious and in considerable pain,
he showed no immediate sign of tears to his rescuers. The
firefighters and ambulance crew took one look at the boy's
predicament and decided to rush Salim and mincing
machine straight to hospital.

Once the emergency entourage arrived in the casualty
section of St Mary's Hospital, Salim was gently laid down
upon a trolley and the mincing machine carefully put
alongside the boy. As a medical team rapidly examined
the lad, he still refused to show his feelings.

It was decided that because of the sheer bulk of the
mincer, the use of an operating theatre was not practical.
The examination room of the casualty department was
then prepared for the extrication attempt. Whilst this
work went ahead, Salim's pain was eased by drugs, yet
still he remained tear-free, although as two firefighters
prepared their cutting gear out of sight of Salim on the
trolley, the boy did speak for the first time.

'Take it off, Mister, it hurts!' was his impassioned plea.

Once the doctors were ready, Salim was given a general
anaesthetic and the job of sawing through the heavy metal
casting of the machine funnel began. The fire crews
worked in relays for it was laboriously hot under the
bright white lights. Using hacksaws with very gentle pressure and short, precise strokes, they slowly worked around
the circular shape of the funnel until it was about three
quarters through. Taking great care not to cut into Salim's
forearm, the cutting operation then had to be slowed
down until, after an hour's team effort, the mincer funnel
was parted. Then after some critically careful turning of

the gear wheels within the machine itself, Salim's hand was finally free.

The fire crews backed away to allow the doctors to examine his entire hand and wrist, but within a few seconds it was clear to all around that Salim's hand could not be saved. An amputation was needed. As the firefighters picked up their tools and equipment, there was a sad atmosphere, especially after the boy had shown such courage.

However, the story of Salim had two happier sequels. The first was that during the following night the same crew of firefighters, now on night duty, were called to St Mary's Hospital to deal with a small fire in piles of rubbish in a yard. After it had been extinguished, the Station Officer enquired in the casualty department of Salim's condition. Although it was nearing midnight, the fire officer was taken upstairs to the ward where Salim lay. The boy was awake.

'Hello, Salim,' whispered the Station Officer. 'How are you?'

'I'm all right,' replied the plucky lad. 'Where are all the other firemen?'

'They're all downstairs and I'll tell them how you're getting on,' he said, now conscious of being in his full firefighting rig although he had taken his fire helmet off.

In the dimmed light of the children's ward he could see that Salim's left arm was swathed in a large white dressing before the sister alongside him nodded towards the door.

The second part of the story took place some weeks later after Salim had been finally discharged from hospital. The entire watch of firemen at Paddington fire station prepared a very special surprise for the boy.

Salim was collected from his home in a fire brigade staff car and taken to the fire station. There he looked over all the fire engines, sat behind their steering wheels, rang their bells, and sounded the two tone horns. He tried on a fire helmet and watched the fire crews as they slid down the poles and took a fire engine out into the yard to pitch ladders and get water jets to work.

Then Salim was taken up to the mess room where the watch had prepared a party spread with balloons. Afterwards, Salim looked a trifle overwhelmed and so too, did most of the firemen!

6
Sparks amid the Smoke

Firefighters as can already be seen, really do have to develop a finely tuned sense of humour and fun which serves to offset the often traumatic side of their daily work. One much revered London Fire Brigade senior officer likened a fireman to being a 'connoisseur of human misfortune' and few experienced firefighters would disagree with this apt description.

For apart from fire incidents, fire crews are often amongst the first on the scene of road and railway crashes, industrial accidents and the occasional domestic tragedy. They work amid frequent scenes of death and serious injury, tending and comforting the live casualties and, later, extricating and releasing trapped bodies with a gentle reverence and respect. Many of the fires extinguished by firefighters will be caused by sheer negligence and carelessness, as will a number of the non-fire emergencies they attend. The human suffering they regularly witness at fires and accidents at such close hand must not interfere with the firefighting and rescue efforts, and every firefighter has to develop a detachment from the scenes of death and injury which can confront them almost every day and night.

Were it not, therefore, for the humour of the service and the ability to laugh at oneself, the demands upon firefighters everywhere would be close to unbearable. However, the close knit camaraderie of the fire station watch brings about a constantly developing sense of teamwork, in which sharing the operational experiences and achievements of the watch all help to mould a highly professional yet human team. This is often enhanced by some of the larger-than-life characters who are attracted to the diversities of a firefighter's life.

During my period of service in London as a station commander at Paddington fire station, I came across one such gem of a personality. He came to Paddington on transfer as a Leading Fireman and was known to us all on the watch as 'Norm'.

Norm had come to the watch as a relative stranger, a Leading Fireman from the South East London division at Lewisham. A dark haired, swarthy six-footer, he soon found himself quite at home in the newly opened Paddington fire station which had replaced two Victorian fire stations at Edgware Road and Kilburn. Soon the whole watch came to wonder at the many talents of 'Big Norm' who was a marvellous example of a firefighter's need to be a jack of all trades.

A typical 'for instance' was his car – a rather jaded, ten year old plus model. Norm would say, 'I don't wash it, I sheep-dip it!' This vehicle had, to say the least, seen much better days, but was a workshop on wheels, with a wonderful variety of tools that the AA would have been proud to own. Norm's standard method of starting his car appeared to be by short-circuiting a piece of wire across the battery terminals to the starter solenoid!

About this time, I personally suffered the indignity of a slight blemish on the otherwise gleaming paintwork of my own car, after an argument with a bollard. Norm just happened to let drop the remark that this too was in his line. Out then, one night duty, came the panel beating tools, some very rusty, many bent and some just unrecognisable! But very soon the dent had gone and paint appeared over the bare metal area, thanks to certain fire brigade airline equipment that was not designed as spraying gear, but it did the job.

Watch technical lectures too, took on a new dimension with Norm's graphic visual aids – one session, I recall, somehow digressed into the subject of slaughterhouses, very gory and all from personal experience!

Operationally, on the fireground Norm was worth his weight in gold, purely for his inventive genius, which sometimes could mean sailing very close to the wind, either procedurally, or from a public relations standpoint.

Such was one instance at the office and warehouse premises of a well known London art auction house in Bayswater. We were turned out by an early morning '999' call to these premises, which were suffering from an over sensitive newly installed automatic fire alarm. We had, in fact, been called to this building several times during the previous days and the layout was well known to all three watches at Paddington. On this occasion, the complex was duly searched via a first floor window, to no avail. However, we could not gain entry into the ground floor entrance lobby containing the fire alarm control panel without forcing a pair of glass doors. Clearly, we did not want to do this as there was no fire situation.

Now whilst the owner was being collected by police from deepest Middlesex at this awful hour, Norm attempted to silence the noise of the outside alarm bell which was still ringing out its shrill tone into the night.

All this activity took place adjacent to a large general hospital and Norm no doubt had the patients welfare at heart. His aim was to reach the 'silence' push-button on the control panel, which was within the ground floor lobby, and in sight through the locked glazed doors. A problem for some, but Norm was original and resourceful as ever. He started assembling the chimney rods together and through the letter box flap of the front door, proceeded to 'fish' for the push-button that would quieten the awful racket. To reach the button on the panel, Norm had to join about eight rods together. Then it happened – the rods, well pushed through at this stage, and stretching out some twenty five feet, became trapped by the letter box spring.

At times like this I was always concious of the brigade's precious image in this modern world, and on the occasions of the previous calls to this building, I had personally assured the senior manager that his company's precious oil and watercolour paintings, carvings and art materials, were well protected by the London Fire Brigade and his new alarm system.

Consequently, the sight of the manager turning up in dressing gown at 0300 hours on this dark and wet morning with the alarm bell ringing and a firefighter hanging on the end of a considerable number of chimney rods which disappeared into his letter box, was really too awful to contemplate!

Suffice to say however, that by the time the manager did arrive, Norm had safely freed all the rods and removed them. He later even managed to straighten the letter box flap. The alarm bell rang on until we opened up the building with the manager's keys and reset the entire system. And I resolved never to let Norm try this stunt ever again.

Norm also had a lovely turn of phrase when the occasion demanded it. One night duty, he was one of Paddington's Pump crew which had gone as a reinforcing fire engine onto North Kensington's fire station area to provide assistance at a 'persons reported' fire – one where the '999' caller had said people could be trapped by the fire and the smoke.

As we turned off Ladbroke Grove and sped into Lancaster Road, North Kensington firefighters were already bringing people trapped above the fire down the wheeled escape ladder pitched into the third floor of some terraced tenements. Dark smoke was plumming up from the windows at first floor level and we quickly ran over to assist the rescue operations.

Norman and I took over the control of the escape ladder down which several pyjama and nighty-clad men and women were already descending, assisted by a North Kensington firefighter. This freed the single firefighter at the base of the ladder to rejoin his colleagues now concentrating on firefighting inside the flats, leaving one other North Kensington fireman at the window above from where a man and a woman, holding a child, were climbing out onto the escape ladder.

'Any more for the skylark?' called out Norman as he started to climb up the ladder past those coming down. As he did so, there was an almighty crash on the pavement right alongside me. A large suitcase had been thrown out of the top window. This was closely followed by another. Someone up there was intent on bringing their personal belongings with them.

This was too much for Norman, who was by now about halfway up the ladder to the woman at the window with the baby in her arms.

'If you want a porter, lady, you'd best go to Waterloo Station. Now leave 'yer cases and come down peacefully!'

It was an exquisite and spontaneous piece of fire service humour, during what could have developed into a serious fire. Fortunately, the outbreak was contained within the first floor bedroom where it had started, although there was severe smoke damage throughout the building. The fire had started after some cooking pans had been left on, which then ignited some nearby curtains.

There were no serious casualties amongst the West Indian residents of the flat, although Norm did reflect afterwards that I could so easily have been wounded in battle by a most unusual hazard – flying luggage!

Before my spell as a watch commander at Paddington, I spent over a year in a similar role at Kensington fire station. This was a very busy station then answering about 2,000 '999' calls per year with the three fire engines based there. Kensington fire station was a Victorian building located up a narrow mews in Old Court Place, just off Kensington High Street. What was sufficient accomodation for horse drawn steam fire pumps and their brass helmeted crews back in 1895, was hardly suitable for modern day firemen and their large fire engines.

The training facilities were abysmally inadequate, as the drill tower in the tiny yard at the rear of the station was only of three floors in height and very inaccessible. Inside, Kensington fire station was like many of its aged counterparts in the London Fire Brigade, having white glazed tiling to the entire walls of the engine bays, offices, staircases, kitchen and mess, and other accommodation. With tiles everywhere one looked, it was rather like working in a huge public lavatory.

There were even several relics from the horse drawn days. Some of the old stables where the fire horses waited for their summons to action were still in use as storerooms, whilst hanging from the ceiling above the three gleaming red fire engines were the shackles and other fittings from where the harnesses had been suspended over the shafts of the steam pumps. Kensington also boasted its two lovely original much polished brass poles, down which we all cascaded if a shout came in whilst the duty crews were on the first floor of the fire station. Although it was an old building, most firemen liked the place. Kensington had a special atmosphere for me if only due to the sense of firefighting history that pervaded the entire building.

But it was not an easy fire station to operate from. In particular, the turnout to '999' calls down the narrow mews and out into four lanes of slow moving and constantly busy London traffic was a regular nightmare for fire engine drivers and other motorists alike.

One special incident only a hundred yards from the doors of Kensington fire station illustrated this only too well, and although it was a potentially serious at the time, I think all the firemen involved had a good laugh about it once the dust had settled.

It all started one weekday summer morning with the duty crews preparing to end their 15 hour night shift and hand over to the firefighters of the oncoming day shift at 0900 hours. However, as often was the case, a fire call was no respector of shift patterns.

Down in Warwick Road, Earls Court, a shopkeeper thought he saw smoke coming from the hotel at the rear of his shop and rang '999'. Inside thirty seconds, the fire bells were ringing out throughout Kensington fire station and the teleprinter link from Control was buzzing out the details of the address. All three fire engines, Pump Escape,

Pump and Turntable Ladder, were ordered. In no time at all, the three red doors of the fire station crashed open to reveal a blaze of white headlights and blue flashing light from the rotating beacons.

The firemen climbed into their mounts, two tone horns hooted into life and the fire engines took off in single file, led by the Pump Escape, and followed by the Turntable Ladder, and then the Pump. As usual at this time of morning, the junction out into Kensington High Street was choked with buses, taxis, lorries and cars but with deft skill, and some assistance from other drivers, the Pump Escape driver nudged into a gap and moved slowly across the High Street and started to swing his fire engine right towards Earls Court.

Then it all started to go wrong. The Turntable Ladder, second in the procession behind the Pump Escape, had a projecting overhang in front of the cab of about twelve foot of the telescoped ladder sections. As the Pump Escape driver began his right turn through the traffic at no more than about 5 mph, he was suddenly confronted by a car which pulled out of line in the opposite traffic queue. The Pump Escape driver had to just momentarily touch his brakes and as the first fire engine almost slowed to a halt, disaster struck.

For the overhanging section at the front of the Turntable Ladder, which was rather too close behind, almost imperceptibly made contact with the back end of the wheeled ladder on the rear of the Pump Escape. As the two fire engines touched, the big nozzle at the very front of the Turntable's overhang jammed into the various steel cables of the Pump Escape extending gear. The two red giants were now locked together.

But worse was to follow. Whilst the Turntable Ladder driver was only too aware of his plight, the fireman driving the Pump Escape ahead certainly was not, and completely unaware that he was now towing the twelve ton mass of the second fire engine behind, he started to accelerate away towards Earls Court with his warning horns blaring.

As he did so, the massive force being exerted between the two fire engines snapped off the device which locked the telescopic ladder sections of the Turntable Ladder when not in operation. As the Pump Escape pulled away, it pulled out about twenty feet of telescopic ladder section before the urgent hooting and shouts from both the Turntable Ladder crew and many motorists alerted the Pump Escape crew to their dilemma.

By the time the two connected fire engines came to a halt about thirty yards further on, they were effectively blocking most of Kensington High Street. Between the two vehicles was a horizontal metal bridge formed by the groaning and flexing metal ladder. As both crews climbed down and took stock of the incredible situation, it was clear that they were not going to any more emergency calls on this shift of duty.

Fortunately, the third fire engine was quite unaffected by the drama being played out in front, and its driver and Leading Fireman in charge had the presence of mind to turn left out into the traffic throng, and battle up towards the first set of traffic lights on a indirect route to Earls Court and the '999' call still awaiting an attendance.

This remaining Kensington crew arrived at Earls Court some seven minutes or so later, in company with two fire engines from Chelsea which had been alerted when the two Kensington crews were clearly not able to proceed due to their altercation. After a rapid reconnaissance, it became clear that the fire call was a 'good intent' false alarm. The caller had certainly seen smoke emitting from the hotel roof but it was simply from a boiler in need of servicing.

Back at Kensington High Street, the scene was chaotic. Although traffic police were quickly upon the scene, it took over half an hour before the two fire engines could be untangled by London Fire Brigade engineering staff. The Pump Escape was easily driveable, having sustained most damage to its wheeled ladder. The Turntable Ladder, however, posed a great difficulty with the twenty feet or so of ladder extended horizontally over its bonnet. It was only possible to partly rehouse the metal sections as it had obviously suffered from some distortion and twisting.

As Kensington High Street was temporarily closed, the Turntable Ladder was carefully manoeuvred under its own power back up Old Court Place and into the fire station bays. It was not possible to close the outer doors as the fire engine was still longer than when it had left on the last shout! Later in the day, it was taken to Lambeth Workshops and replaced by a reserve vehicle.

Once the two damaged fire engines were inside Kensington fire station, both the duty crew and the oncoming day watch noisily surrounded the two vehicles to inspect the damage. There followed a certain amount of boisterous hilarity, especially towards the two firemen drivers involved. This was, perhaps, not only a thankful reaction that no one had been injured, but also more likely gave vent to some of the black humour that is always part of the fire service. There was the suggestion that the drama played out earlier in the High Street was part of a new policy of saving fuel costs by joining two fire engines together!

Implausible though this was, the London *Evening Standard* carried the story of the argument between two of Kensington's fire engines. Even after the subsequent official enquiry had concluded that part mechanical failure and part driver error were to blame, the two drivers concerned took a long time to live down what was, by any standards, a most unusual traffic accident.

At the time I had some sympathy for them both, for a few years earlier, whilst at Manchester Square fire station just behind Selfridge's in London's Oxford Street, I was the driver of an old pre-war open style Leyland Turntable Ladder on a short journey I shall never forget.

This veteran fire engine was one of several remaining which had seen service right through the London Blitz. By the late 1960's they were at the end of their operational life with their dated mechanisms compared to modern aerial fire engines. They were normally only called into front-line use as reserve vehicles when the more modern turntable ladders were being serviced, as was the case with Manchester Square's new aerial ladder.

Once our new Turntable Ladder was back from workshops, my task was to drive the old ladder to its normal location as a reserve vehicle – Acton fire station. It was a rainy late midweek afternoon when I swung the venerable old Leyland out into the West End traffic. Despite the rain dripping off my cap and down the neck of my black waterproof topcoat, the veteran was a delight to drive. For one thing many heads turned at the approach of an open fire engine of such massive bulk. The Leyland also had a lovely booming exhaust note although it had very heavy steering and a real beast of a crash gearbox.

But on this occasion my trip to West London was destined not to last long. For I had only got as far as the slow moving traffic of Marble Arch, when the old petrol engined Leyland started misfiring each time it pulled away from a stop.

And then, the unthinkable happened. As I turned left into Bayswater Road, and accelerated the twelve ton open fire engine away, the misfiring suddenly grew worse and great sheets of orange flame blew out of the vents on each side of the fire engine's long bonnet. There was also a very strong smell of petrol, and as soon as was possible I halted the Leyland at the kerbside. Climbing down, my worst fears were confirmed. The veteran's engine was on fire underneath its bonnet.

Fortunately, the fire was confined to burning petrol droplets from the carburettors and using the fire extinguisher on board, I was able to snuff the flames out fairly easily. By this time, there was already a long tailback of traffic stretching back around Marble Arch. After all, who wants to go near a burning vehicle, let alone a burning fire engine?

One chivalrous taxi driver going in the opposite direction, towards Oxford Street, did stop and come over to offer some assistance to me.

'Got it out, mate?' he smilingly enquired. He was about my own age and had his cab extinguisher in his hand ready to do his bit.

'Yes, thanks,' I replied, as confidently as I could. 'I've got it out, OK. It's a leaking fuel pipe, I think. No serious damage. I'll call up our mobile engineers.'

'Oh, that's good,' he said. 'I think it was this old lady which did exactly the same to me going to a fire last month when it was on the run at Whitechapel!'

He paused and then went on, 'But, it was OK when it went back to Acton.'

He was, of course, an off duty London fireman working, as a number did, as black cab drivers.

'Cheers, mate!' he called as he dodged the traffic queues now hoping to squeeze past the Leyland fire engine.

As he got to his cab parked half up on the pavement opposite, he added:

'Best place for that thing is a bloody museum. Good luck!' And as I waited alongside the Leyland for the breakdown crew, and watched the curious looks of the passing motorists, I had to agree with his sentiment.

But this embarrassing event was as of nothing compared to the fate of my Blue Watch colleagues at Manchester Square fire station, located at No 1 Chiltern Street, W1, just behind Selfridges in Oxford Street.

It was during a very busy operational spell over one Sunday night duty. Manchester Square ran two Pumps and a Turntable Ladder.

At that time, a suppertime meal for the twelve firefighters of the nightshift was usually prepared by the daytime cook. All the night watch had to do was put it in the oven. But on this evening, the designated 'mess manager' had decided to prepare some chips. Although it was normal to drop this firefighter off his crew for the duration of his preparation and cooking duties, this had not been possible due to low crew numbers.

There followed three separate, sequential '999' calls, within about four minutes, each to a different address in the West End. Thus, the three fire engines roared off into the night, leaving the station empty but in the care of George, a lone watchroom attendant.

George was one of a group of six retired London firemen, now engaged on communication duties who manned the Manchester Square watchroom adjacent to the engine house on the ground floor, 24 hours a day, due to its status as a Divisional HQ.

After all the three fire engines had clamorously turned out, George pushed the button to close the big front bay doors and got on with his telephones and teleprinters. In the watchroom background, the brigade radio crackled out its various messages from all the fire engines mobile and dealing with fire calls in the West End and North London area.

Some five minutes passed and George's attention was still engaged with the rolls of teleprinter messages, when the station enquiry bell rang. George got up and opened the door onto the pavement of Chiltern Street, to be confronted by a well dressed elderly woman, who burst out in an excited tone.

'Get the firemen, quickly, it's on fire!'

George was used to taking the occasional 'running fire call' at Manchester Square. These were when smoke was seen, or a fire alarm heard in the busy streets around the fire station, and someone actually ran to physically alert the firemen to the emergency close by.

'Where is the fire, madam?' asked George, calmly and quickly. 'Where exactly is it?'

The woman pointed directly upwards over her head and cried out, 'Up above you, on the first floor. Quickly, your fire station is on fire!'

And so it was. George swung round and looked up unbelievingly and, sure enough, there was fairly thick smoke wafting out of the open first floor windows.

George ran back to his watchroom as fast as he could go and rang Wembley Fire Control on his direct line.

'Manchester Square here. There's a fire on the first floor. All machines are out. Get a pump here bloody quick!'

Then he went cautiously up the stairs to the first floor. There was no sign or smell of fire, but as soon as he got to the half landing his fireman's nose caught the first wiff of smoke in the air, and the familiar crackling, from deep within the mess and kitchen area, as the flames took hold. He checked the kitchen door was closed. George knew no one was inside as all the duty firefighters were out on the various '999' calls. The fire was too serious for him to tackle on his own, so he went back down to the watchroom and rang the residents of several flats at the back of the fire station complex. By now, other passers by were ringing the emergency bell frantically. As he put the telephone down, George thankfully noticed that one of the teleprinters was already telling of the despatch of two fire engines from Soho fire station to 'a fire at Manchester Square fire station.' At this time of night they would not be long, five or six minutes at most.

By the time George got out into Chiltern Street to brief the oncoming Soho firefighters, he could hear the very welcome sound of two tone horns in the distance. For the smoke now pouring out of the two open front windows was a thick black colour and a deep, flickering, orange flame was visible from inside the room.

There was quite a sizeable crowd gathered as the two Soho pumps drew up. One team of firefighters pulled out hose and pitched a ladder to the first floor, whilst the other crew in breathing apparatus took a hose line up the stairs to attack the fire at close quarters.

George watched all this animated activity with a fireman's critical eye and thought about all the paperwork that would inevitably flow from this dreadful and embarrassing outbreak.

Within five minutes, George could tell that the Soho

crews had extinguished the fire on the first floor kitchen. The dark smoke was turning to steam and more windows were being opened to ventilate the fire station. One more fire statistic had been successfully dealt with, even if it was at a unusual site – *at a fire station*!

What is not recorded about this incident is the reactions of the three Manchester Square crews as they, one by one, returned from their various emergency calls, only to find Soho firefighters clearing up at No 1 Chiltern Street.

Neither is George's retort to the Blue Watch mess manager, who sheepishly admitted to failing to turn off the deep fat fryer in the kitchen before dashing out on one of the fire calls. The fat had got so hot it caught fire, and the flames had spread to the kitchen curtains and then across the polystyrene ceiling tiles.

The Blue Watch Station Officer was none too pleased with the miscreant either, for although the fire damage was confined to the cooker area, the noxious and toxic smoke from the burning plastic tiles had coated the kitchen and its contents with a sticky and foul smelling, black film.

There was an inquiry, of course, where disciplinary action was involved, and urgent reminders were issued to all London firefighters to ensure this saga was not repeated elsewhere.

The next day, the London *Evening Standard* carried a brief story of the fire in the fire station. And in the way of these things, the mess manager culprit soon discovered that he had gained an overnight notoriety, which was to stay with him throughout his service career.

Life as a firefighter in central London at this time certainly had its fair share of surprises. This was still the time of the Cold War with the then Soviet bloc. But such political differences were of no help to my crew who turned out to the Russian Embassy in Bayswater at about 1 am one frosty January morning.

A policeman on guard duty outside the Embassy had noticed a large refuse bin burning close to the garages on one side of the drive of the large detached Victorian mansion, which overlooked Hyde Park.

My crew were soon outside the Embassy, which was on a very secure site, surrounded by a high wire fence. By the time of our arrival, flames from the refuse bin were some ten feet high and it was five minutes or so before two plain clothed Russians escorts appeared, both carrying automatic weapons, and opened the gates leading into the drive. We were then able to drive our fire engine down to the garages to douse the flames. The Russians, presumably KGB guards, stood over us as we went about our work. The large wheeled metal bin was full up with various papers and shredded documents, and to extinguish the deep seated fire, it was necessary to tip all the contents out and sift through them carefully, using a hose reel spray, and then replacing the scorched pile back in the bin. This messy task took about half an hour throughout which time the two expressionless Russians said absolutely nothing. We were glad to have the Metropolitan Police officer with us for moral support as the damping down continued in the face of two very similar and deadly looking guns. Great care was taken to replace every piece of dampened rubbish back in the bin before washing the area down, making our gear up and retreating back onto British soil once again, not at all sure if our efforts had contributed to Anglo Soviet relations or not!

Another unusual occurence, this time whilst I was doing a short stint as Station Officer at Kensington fire station, followed a brief spell when due to a boiler fault, Kensington fire station was without hot water and shower facilities. Repairs dragged on and arrangements were made for duty crews to keep a change of clothing on the fire engines. In event of a shower becoming necessary following firefighting operations, the Kensington crews would go to the much newer Chelsea fire station.

As the boiler saga entered another weekend, we steeled ourselves to this rather unsatisfactory arrangement, when

there came a fire call to the nearby five star Royal Garden
Hotel in Kensington High Street.

A small fire had been discovered by the hotel security
staff in some pipework lagging in the hotel basement
boiler room. We quickly put the smoldering fire out, but
were then faced with a lot of careful cutting away of the
glowing embers of the fire, which had spread into the
maze of other lagged pipes feeding the hotel tower block
above. This work was obviously going to take some time
and the usual 'detained' radio message was sent to Control. A sprinkler head had actuated in the boiler room
and with all our cutting away operations which disturbed
quite a lot of dust, the two crews were soon transformed
into very wet and grimy figures.

Now as officer in charge, I happened at this juncture
to mention to the duty hotel manager that we were without hot water back at the fire station. Our normal relation-
ship with this hotel was always excellent, but on this
occasion, they quite surpassed themselves. Leaving the
two least wet firemen to watch over the fire area, the
remainder of the crews were led upstairs into the sumptu-
ous hotel foyer and here fire boots and leggings were
removed for the sake of the carpets. Then we were ushered
into an unoccupied private suite where we were allowed
to make full use of the shower and bath facilities.

In addition, one of the hotel snack bars was specially
opened up and coffee, tea and sandwiches were all laid
on along with full table service. Naturally, we enjoyed
every minute of this unexpected treat but all too soon it
was time to return to the foyer, collect our boots and
leggings, and return to Kensington fire station. Everyone
was profuse with thanks to the hotel manager and his
staff for such considerate treatment at this early hour.

The sequel to this saga was that eventually during that
week, a new boiler arrived and was fitted at the fire
station. It was sheer delight to have hot water again, and
from then on for a few weeks, every time I ran a shower
after a dirty 'job', I remembered the rows of grubby fire

boots in one corner of the foyer of one of London's most prestigious hotels in the early hours of that cold April morning.

There are the rare occasions in the rich variety that is a firefighter's experience, when a fire actually comes to a fire station! This has twice happened to me during my own career.

The first such incident was during my London Fire Brigade years at Manchester Square fire station. We had not long returned from a fire call, which had transpired to be a malicious false alarm, and were busily engaged upon washing down the fire engines. Suddenly, a City of Westminster refuse truck pulled up right outside the fire station with a screech and hissing of its brake system.

This did not excite much attention until the driver and his mate got down, and I noticed that there was a blue smoke haze lazily drifting upwards out of the open back of the vehicle, which was very full of West End rubbish. The refuse truck was carrying a mobile fire deep inside its compacted contents, possibly started by a cigarette end coming into contact with some dry paper.

The driver of the truck was all for us putting out the fire there and then, but it really was not practical to allow him to disgorge twenty tons of general rubbish out into Chiltern Street W1, in order to allow us to damp down the burning load. Twenty tons of wet rubbish would take some putting back into the truck, and none of us relished the task.

After some persuasion by our Station Officer, the driver accepted that his truck would not burst into flames there and then, and that the oxygen starved, smouldering fire would not develop very quickly.

There followed a strange procession of a London fire engine with its two tones and blue lights flashing, preceeding a City of Westminster refuse truck through the traffic to the council depot a mile or so away. To keep the council driver happy, two firefighters rode with him and by the time the truck swung into the depot yard, the smoke coming from the rear of the truck was getting thicker.

The rubbish container was elevated and the load was slowly tipped out. As part of the contents spilled onto the ground, there was a mini flashover amongst some cardboard boxes and paper rolls as the load burst into flame.

It took about thirty minutes for us to completely damp the rubbish pile down, thankful that a nearby council digger would replace the damp and smelly load which had become another, if unusual, London fire statistic.

The second instance of a fire coming to a fire station took place at the Kempston headquarters of Bedfordshire Fire Service which is situated adjacent to the main St. Pancras–Sheffield Inter-City railway line.

The complex housed the Brigade's twenty four hour Fire Control, from where all '999' emergency calls in the county were handled. Also on the site is a fire station which was permanently manned during the daytime hours. However, nightime '999' calls were answered by crews responding on the sounding of their 'bleepers' from their homes nearby.

At about 0400 hours one autumn morning, the staff in Control heard a train hooting rather loudly on the railway lines at the back of the complex. This was very unusual at this hour, but nobody thought it of any significance until some five minutes had passed when there was a frantic hammering on the outside windows of the Control suite.

Before one of the male staff could investigate the noise, a buzzer on the main panel indicated that someone outside had found the illuminated red telephone set into the outside doorway, which was a direct line to the Control panel inside.

'Thank God, someone's here! I was giving up. Come quick!' came a voice from the panel loudspeaker. 'My train is on fire. At the back!'

And it was too. Although Control immediately alerted the duty crew who quickly drove the two Kempston fire engines into the fire station drill yard which bordered the railway lines, one set of bogie wheels of the class 47 diesel electric locomotive was burning fiercely. Worse still, driven by the chill wind the orange flames were beginning to lick the end of the first carriage of the train, which transpired to be full of newspapers destined for Derby and Nottingham.

Fortunately, a rapid attack with dry powder and water spray soon had the fire out, by which time the breathless driver, a stocky, elderly balding man, had explained his predicament. He had been driving trains on this line for fifteen years or so and well knew of the location of the fire station as he often flashed past at 100 mph.

On this occasion, he had sensed all was not well as the north-bound train emerged from Ampthill tunnel, some four miles from Kempston fire station. He had looked back down the newspaper train and seen flames at the rear bogie of the locomotive. Rather than stop his train in a very remote spot thereabouts, he decided to reduce speed, yet continue to where he knew firefighter help would be on hand at Kempston, several minutes up the line.

What he had not reckoned on was that the fire station would be in darkness and at night manned by firefighters on standby from their houses nearby. Neither was the train driver aided by having to scale a fence and stumble around in the dark to finally find the well lit *front* entrance which, of course, was designed to serve motorists and pedestrians from the normal direction.

After the fire was out it took an hour or so for the railway managers to organize another locomotive to move the disabled, fire damaged one. Eventually, both Derby, Nottingham and the East Midlands got their London newspapers rather late that day, and one British Rail driver had cause to recall his unusual encounter with Bedfordshire firefighters and the night that he took his train to the fire station.

7

Creatures Great and Small

It is quite remarkable just what a wide variety of emergency calls to the fire brigade originate when animals of all shapes and sizes get into some sort of trouble.

Looking back on my fire service years, the most common animal incident tended to be recalcitrant cats stuck up trees. After the Second World War, firemen continued to pit their wits against such felines but in 1950, a Sheffield firefighter suffered a fatal fall out of a high tree whilst trying to carry out a cat rescue.

Since then it became accepted national practice for all 'cat up tree' 999 calls to be first referred to the RSPCA. Their officers, having assessed the particular situation, decide if firefighters and their ladders are necessary and if this is the case, a rescue operation is quickly mounted.

Cats, however, never seem to appreciate efforts to get them down from the lofty perches high up in trees or on roof tops to where they have usually persued their feathered prey.

One particularly unappreciative cat lived with its elderly lady owner in a luxury flat in St John's Wood, close to Lord's Cricket Ground. The animal, a long haired grey Persian, had apparently taken off some hours earlier about eighty feet up into the upper branches of a slim tree in the courtyard of the apartment block. The rather distressed lady owner had called the RSPCA and with dusk approaching, hoped that something could be done to get her 'little boy' down.

The RSPCA officer had asked for fire service assistance when it was immediately obvious from his own appraisal of the situation that the feline was far too high up the tree for him to reach. Fortuitously, as it was winter time,

▲A 1954 view of an Auxiliary Fire Service exercise in the Lambeth drillyard of London Fire Brigade headquarters. The AFS Green Goddess Bedford fire engine is pumping about 1,000 gallons per minute. The crews are still wearing wartime issue steel helmets.
(*London Fire Brigade*)

▼Southwark training school recruits hook ladder squad, 1964. The fireman is attached to the lower ladder only by a metal hook on his special belt. A second recruit is just out of sight below. Strength, control and balance are all needed as there are five more floors to go! (*London Fire Brigade*)

▲ A unique fire service occasion. Eight Turntable Ladders rehearse at Lambeth headquarters in 1968 for the finale of a Royal visit. This involved the unfurling of Union Jacks and LFB flags at 100 feet. The TL on the far right is the fire engine which the author had a few adventures with whilst serving at Manchester Square fire station.

(London Fire Brigade)

▼ A 1965 view of the first fire engine the author drove to a '999' call – the Dennis Pump Escape at Croydon's Old Town fire station. These models had a Rolls Royce 5.6 litre petrol engine and a swine of a gearbox. The 50 foot wheeled escape is of an all-metal pattern. *(Author's collection)*

A fine example of a modern fire engine – a 1992 Dennis Rapier. With low chassis, turbo-powered diesel with auto gearbox, power steering and crew safety cab, it is a far cry from its predecessors. *(Dennis Specialist Vehicles)* ▼

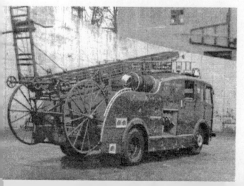

▲There is never a typical road traffic accident but this view of a road crash in East Devon shows the struggle to free a badly trapped driver after a collision between a lorry and car. 21 August 1989   (*Mark Wilkins*)

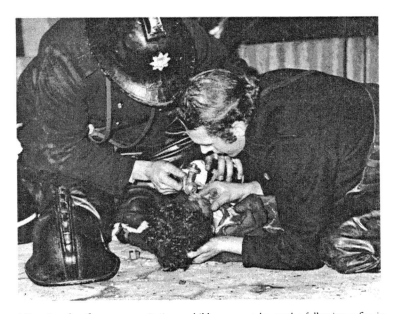

▲Two London firemen resuscitating a child overcome by smoke following a fire in residential flats near the Elephant & Castle, South London. 10 December 1971.
(*Owen Rowlands*)

▲ Two views of the aftermath of a large fire at Grocers' Hall in the City of London. 200 firefighters fought the fire and although they prevented its spread to nearby buildings close to the Bank of England, the ornate livery hall was badly damaged. 22 September 1965   (*London Fire Brigade*)

▲ A London Fire Brigade Hose Layer showing the method of flaking the hose ready to be laid out on the move. It was on a similar specialist fire engine from Chelsea fire station that the author first encountered Fireman Colin Comber only weeks before he was killed.
(London Fire Brigade)

▶ An elderly couple died amid the smoke of a serious fire in this block of dwellings. The author was one of the three man crew first on the scene and attempted a rescue by hook ladder which is still in position. The fire is now all but out and the reinforcing crews have things under control. Crawford Street, W1. 14 October 1969.
(London Fire Brigade)

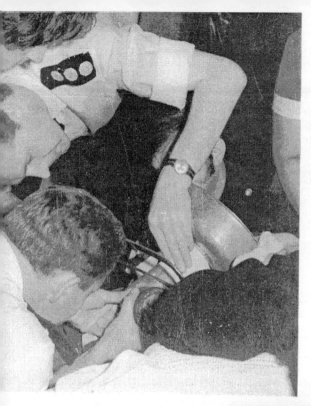

◄A team of firefighters at work on the rescue of Salim – a young boy with his fingers and hand trapped in a mincing machine. Here a very careful effort to saw through the mincer outer shell is under way. St. Mary's Hospital Casualty Unit, Paddington, London, W2. 12 June 1970.

(*London Fire Brigade*)

►Another challenging 'child' rescue. Three year old Lola has got her index finger jammed under the handle of a luggage trolley, and here fire crews are cutting through the trolley frame whilst nurses read a story to the little girl. University College Hospital Casualty Unit, London, WC1. 1 February 1978.

(*London Fire Brigade*)

▲Not for the faint-hearted. Two firefighters have plunged into the River Lea to retrieve a distressed horse which has fallen into the water. Note the improvised use of fire service hose and lines guiding the animal to the safety of the river bank. Ferry Lane, Tottenham, London, N17. 28 September 1984. (*London Fire Brigade*)

▼Manchester Square fire station, Chiltern Street, London, W1, just off Oxford Street, where the author served for several eventful years. The station was opened in 1904 and in this 1968 photograph still displays the fine original bay door stonework carvings which were later removed during modernisation. The greengrocer's blind is opposite the bay nearest the camera. (*London Fire Brigade*)

▲ The Leinster Towers Hotel fire in London's Bayswater from which 45 residents were rescued after fire broke out on the fourth floor soon after dawn. Note the wheeled escapes and hook ladders in use as over 100 firefighters finally get the upper hand. 6 June 1969   (*London Fire Brigade*)

▼ The dramatic rescue of firefighters by firefighters. Inside the room at the head of the ladder four firemen lay buried amid burning debris after the roof had suddenly fallen in, just as the fire was coming under control. One of the crew was killed and two others seriously burned. It was three hours before they were all released. Note the scorching around the windows. The author is on the balcony calling down. The Worsley Hotel, London, W9. 13 December 1974   (*London Fire Brigade*)

The value of fire doors was well illustrated at the Worsley Hotel fire. An arsonist had lit several fires on different levels and despite severe damage to all floors, the fire has not spread beyond this point.   (*London Fire Brigade*) ▼

The funerals of the five firefighters killed in the Dudgeons Wharf explosion, with the first of the coffins being carried into church at Stratford, East London.

(London Fire Brigade)

▲ Shocked passengers mill around in this crash scene soon after a returning seaside excursion train has been derailed at speed. The first fire, police and medical rescue teams are arriving and some semblance of command and control will shortly be set up. Eltham Well Hall, South London, SE9. 11 June 1972   *(London Fire Brigade)*

▲The aftermath at London's Heathrow airport after a Vanguard aircraft landing with a cargo of racehorses crashed into the buildings of Terminal 1 (behind the fire engine far left distance). Two Tridents of the then British European Airways had their tails sliced clean off. The trail of wreckage was awesome. 3 July 1968. (*London Fire Brigade*)

▶Nowadays, a number of hazardous chemicals in industrial use, or in storage or transit, are so dangerous that firefighters require special personal protection. This space-age suit totally encloses the firefighter who is also wearing his breathing set inside. (*Respirex*)

▼Special services calls come in all shapes and forms. Here a mass of scaffolding has crashed down onto a foreign diplomat's limousine in Whitehall Place, SW1, trapping the diplomat and his driver. Sadly neither survived. 10 November 1969. (*London Fire Brigade*)

▲ Inside the Moorgate tunnel of death – surely one of the most awful special services ever attended by British firefighters. Here crews are working on the compacted wreckage of the tube train. 42 passengers were killed and 76 injured in this accident which involved London fire crews for five days and nights. 2 March 1975.

(*London Fire Brigade*)

▼ Smoke is always a problem for firefighters and even at small fires, large volumes of toxic choking fumes can be released. This view of the early stages of a major fire in a Thameside warehouse show the extent of smoke levels. The bright sunshine has been turned to darkness as nearby Tower Bridge in the left background is almost obscured. Note TL in use and a fireboat (left) providing water from the river. Battlebridge Lane, SE1. 9 August 1971. (*London Fire Brigade*)

▲ Thatched roof fires mean hours of hard, physical toil, well shown in this view of the Cott Inn at Dartington in Devon. Crews on both sides of the roof are working to create a firebreak and isolate the fire from the unaffected end of the structure. 28 August 1989. *(Mark Wilkins)*

▼ The scene at the historic Elizabethan town of Totnes in Devon during a large fire which destroyed part of the town centre. Narrow streets hampered the 100 strong firefighting team but the outbreak was confined after a three hour battle. 4 September 1990. *(Devon Fire & Rescue Service)*

▼ Turnout. The moment when a firefighter's adrenalin really starts to flow. *(London Fire Brigade)*

the cat was clearly visible up in the top section of the leafless tree.

The Pump and Turntable Ladder crews from Paddington fire station then took up the challenge of the 'standard moggy call' and as a shower of rain started to fall, it fell to me to pull on the heavy duty leather gauntlets and climb the extended Turntable Ladder high up to where the cat was perched. I took with me an RSPCA pole and snare.

By the time I had got up to the head of the ladder, clipped my belt on, called into the intercom to the ladder operator far below that I was OK, the rain was fairly running down my neck in rivulets.

Two colleagues were now positioned on the flat roof of the apartment block just above me, in case I opted to grab the cat and then have the ladder swung over to the edge of the roof in order to hand over the animal to their safe hands.

Experience with stranded cats showed that no two situations were ever the same and I eyed him up on a branch only six feet away, reflecting that I had never been a great lover of cats.

But, strange to say, just as I was expecting the cat to bolt further away, he did the reverse. He stood up, stretched in the manner confident cats do, yawned, and came very slowly along the branch towards me, all as if this was an everyday occurrence. I was then able to get the noose of the RSPCA snare over his neck and, as I asked the ladder operator below to sway the ladder in a foot nearer the branch, was able to grab the cat, remove the noose and clutch him safely close to my chest.

As the 'little boy' seemed quite happy in my arms, I asked for the ladder to gently take us both down so that I could personally hand the animal over to its owner. After a steady descent of about a minute, we were both back at ground level where the engine noise of the Turntable Ladder was, as usual, quite pronounced.

As I passed the cat to the elderly lady she burst into tears.

'Oh, thank you! Thank you!' she cried. 'What a naughty boy he's been!'

As she stroked the dripping wet cat he put his ears down and, perhaps startled by all the noise, leapt from her arms. In three bounds he made straight for the same tree. With the speed and skill of a squirrel, the cat shot vertically up the trunk and then out along the same branch from where I had so recently rescued him.

My feelings and, no doubt that of my colleagues, were completely summed up by the ladder operator, Martin, who in his lovely cockney tone said 'Blimey, lady, you ought to have that thing in a circus!'

I am afraid to say that most of the firemen at the scene were laughing, as was the RSPCA officer. The lady owner of the flying cat was not so amused by it all.

But as the rain continued to fall and darkness descended, out came the floodlights and up the ladder I went again. Once more, the cat came to me without any demur but this time, once he was caught by the snare noose, he stayed secure.

Once below again, the RSPCA officer took charge of the cat and its distressed owner and led her off to her flat, the animal still in the noose. We made up all equipment pretty quickly. Not only were we all soaking wet, but I had no intention of going up the Turntable Ladder for a third time at the same incident.

Talking of feline rescues, there is a belief that firefighters have a simple, if crude, method of removing cats from trees. Rumour has it that it involves projecting a powerful firefighting jet of water upwards to dislodge the cat, which then falls, hopefully unharmed, into an outstretched salvage sheet below. I can categorically say that in all my years this direct method was only ever used when the animal's owner was definitely not present!

A somewhat more unusual and dangerous encounter for firemen from Euston and Manchester Square fire stations was with another rather larger clawed animal – a London Zoo panda.

It all started when the two resident red pandas at London Zoo, An-An and Chi-Chi, had been paired by Russian and British zoologists hoping for some breeding success. During the pairing attempt, both animals had escaped into trees in adjacent Regent's Park. An-An, the female, was recaptured without too much difficulty but Chi-Chi turned out to be a very stubborn character.

For several days he was able to roam the treetops without impediment, except for the television and other media reporters in pursuit. On the third day of his freedom, Chi-Chi was obviously getting tired and hungry and came to rest in the centre of three tall but slender trees on the sloping bank of Regent's Canal.

Zoo officials then tried luring Chi-Chi down by spreading various delicacies around the base of the tree. Then they brought An-An to the scene, secure on a lead, to see if some female charm could bring him down to earth. Still, Chi-Chi looked dolefully down upon all those below and refused to budge.

At that stage, the fire service took over and bringing some lateral thinking to the situation and using an extension ladder, a fireman managed to tie a 100 foot line to each of the two outer trees. Each of these was then tied to the back of a small van. The vans were then moved sufficiently to bend the tops of the two trees away from the central tree in which Chi-Chi had taken refuge. His escape route had now been removed.

Zoo staff and firemen next spread a large net out under the panda and tried shaking the tree. Chi-Chi clung on to its slender trunk and looked on those below, his large eyes full of suspicion.

It was decided that the best course of action was to saw off the top half of the tree, panda and all, and allow it to fall into the outstretched net below. The pandas' keeper volunteered to do this and armed with a saw, he ascended the 35 foot ladder which was pitched into the tree, and started to saw away.

This seemed to be the signal for Chi Chi to come to life, for after a good look down at what was beginning to happen below, the panda deftly scrambled head first down through the leaves. But once Chi Chi had passed his keeper on the ladder and reached a branch underneath, the panda decided enough was enough. He stretched up and started clawing quite ferociously at the unfortunate keeper now stranded on the ladder only feet above.

Two firemen immediately went to the keeper's aid, one quickly going up the ladder into the tree armed with the zoo's large net device, whilst the other started to climb the tree trunk itself.

For several minutes it was quite a spectacle. In descending order, there was the panda's keeper, then Chi Chi still clawing upwards, beneath which was a fireman on the ladder just below the panda with net poised at the ready. Then came yet another firefighter actually clinging to the tree trunk just below Chi Chi, trying very hard to distract the panda from attacking the keeper uppermost in the tree.

The tree shook and bent alarmingly, first one way, then the other. Leaves drifted down and twigs flew as Chi Chi resisted his captors. But the animal was visibly tiring and after a very short while, his freedom was at an end. The net went over the panda's head and not without some difficulty, the three captors lowered the struggling panda into a larger net on the ground.

All this animal drama was recorded by both BBC and ITN news crews and as a result, the capture of Chi Chi appeared on the nation's television screens that evening. It was by any standards an unusual animal rescue and certainly one which did not go strictly to plan.

However, despite such unforeseen operational problems with animals in peril, some fire service training in central London at that time was directed at the difficulties of animal rescue, and in particular, to the mass evacuation of horses from stables involved in fire.

In the central London area, there were two large cavalry barracks, one at the Knightsbridge base of the Household Cavalry and the other at the St. John's Wood headquarters of the Royal Horse Artillery. A large number of horses were stabled at both locations. With the special fire risks of stabling, a number of very early morning exercises were staged to give firefighters sufficient confidence to handle a large number of horses in a mock fire situation.

0600 hours one summer morning saw the first of these unusual equine exercises commence. The superb mounts of the Household Cavalry were very frisky and suspicious, despite the close attentions of their normal troopers and grooms. The barracks housed quite a complex of stables and with the fire alarms ringing loudly, the lights were all put out. Then the task was to blindfold each horse, and with the assistance of troopers and grooms, to coax and cajole the steeds through the passageways out into fresh air.

The exercises lasted over an hour and gave every firefighter who took part some valuable equestrian handling experience in an exercise not easily forgotten. Afterwards, many thought as I did that a real fire situation in such large stables full of horses would be an absolute nightmare, especially with the added lethal ingredient of smoke and heat.

Single horses in trouble were, perhaps, likely to be more straightforward to deal with. Just occasionally, horses would become stuck in deep mud whilst grazing and their extrication was always a very mucky affair. One such horse rescue took place one wet autumn on the outskirts of East Grinstead during my service in the West Sussex brigade as a Divisional Commander.

It was an unusual emergency in that the horse had become trapped and bogged down whilst still being ridden by a teenage girl. Apparently she had attempted to jump a gate, but her mount had refused, moved sideways and in so doing stumbled up to its knees with all four legs firmly wedged down a deep muddy trench, at the side of what was a very waterlogged field.

Quite coincidentally, as this '999' call was being answered by fire crews from East Grinstead and Turners Hill, I was in the area accompanying the Chief Fire Officer and Her Majesty's Inspector of Fire Services who was in the middle of his week-long annual inspection of the brigade.

The Inspector had just completed his visit to East Grinstead fire station when the duty firefighters were turned out to the horse in distress, and neither the Chief nor HM Inspector could resist following the fire engines to the scene. Having got as close to the location as possible, we were then faced with a half mile trudge along an uneven and muddy bridle path, down which the crews ahead of us were already hurrying various items of equipment.

Now the Inspector had no firefighting uniform with him as his role during the annual inspections was to visit fire stations and witness various exercises. Whilst both the Chief and I had our fire kit with us, neither rigged in it and we quickly followed on after the fire crews ahead in order to see how they dealt with the emergency.

After five minutes or so we came upon the scene, with the distraught teenager trying to reassure her horse as the firemen set to work to free the unfortunate animal. The task was to widen and deepen the offending ditch in order to free the legs of the horse, which by now was beginning to tire from its own efforts to free itself. The danger lay in the animal sitting down into the trench and every effort was put into keeping it up on its legs as the digging operation got under way.

I guided the HMI and the Chief to a small mound close by the stricken horse from where they were able to observe the quiet determination and humane approach to the dilemma. The digging out had to be very carefully done and the ground around the trench soon became a muddy morass several feet deep.

CREATURES GREAT AND SMALL

A vet had by now arrived and pronounced himself satisfied with the rescue attempt progress thus far. After some more careful digging, two canvas strops were passed under the horse's girth and all available hands pulled upwards on either side. The horse pricked up its ears, sensing that something was about to happen, and after several concerted heaves, the animal pulled its forelegs out of the deep mire, rocked on its hind legs and with obvious effort, wrenched itself out of the trench onto firmer ground alongside.

A cheer went up from the twelve or so firefighters present as the girl rider lovingly made a fuss of the horse, whilst the vet quickly ran his hands over the animal's limbs, which he soon pronounced undamaged. As he did so, the horse shook itself violently in a cleaning action, and flung off many fine particles of mud and clay, most of which came in my direction and that of the Chief and HMI!

After congratulating the crews, we three made our way back along the bridleway and its liquid mud towards the waiting staff cars. I felt sure that the incident had demonstrated, far more than any routine exercise, just how well able firefighters could be at adapting their skills and techniques to deal with animal rescues such as this one. The only drawback to the event was the dry cleaning bill to remove some very stubborn Sussex mud from our uniform jackets and trousers, not to mention our shoes. For unlike the fire crews, we could not easily 'wash off' back at the fire engine!

In dealing with animals in trouble, much ingenuity can be called for. A classic incident of its kind involved the rescue of a pig at Stalham, in Norfolk. A 32 stone sow had managed to fall down a 22ft deep well on a farm and was just able to keep afloat when the first firemen of Norfolk Fire Service arrived.

After the well shaft had been floodlit, the crew lassoed the pig and then slowly filled the well shaft up with copious supplies of water fed into the well by several hose lines. As the shaft filled up with water, the sow floated up too, with the firemen keeping a taut line on the animal as she rose higher and higher towards the top of the shaft and safety. Once the sow was level with the top rim of the well, she was able to scramble down and head off to rejoin her two day-old piglets, seemingly none the worse for wear.

But rarely are trapped animals able to co-operate to aid their rescuers and usually the fire service faces a hard physical slog to effect a rescue. Two other West Sussex incidents during my time in that county highlight this.

The first involved two fire crews from Storrington fire station who were called to a heifer which had fallen into a foul smelling farm slurry pit. The struggle to get this animal out, using special sheerlegs erected directly over the slurry pit, was a lengthy operation. At one stage several firemen actually had to get into the thick, pungent liquid in order to secure a strop under the heifer's girth.

After the animal had been successfully hoisted out and washed off, none the worse for wear, it was the firefighters' turn under the hose before they could climb back on board the fire engines! It really was pretty awful. I recall that about six sets of fire uniform actually had to be condemned after this farm incident simply because of the state they were in.

Another West Sussex retained (volunteer) fire station had a particular reputation for animal rescues well carried out. Amongst their 'special' equipment shown to me during my first visit to their fire station was a very long nozzled pepper pot. This was not long after I had arrived in West Sussex, after a career which up until then had been almost entirely that of an inner-city fire officer.

'What do you use that for?' I enquired in a genuinely puzzled tone.

'Well, zur,' replied the Station Officer who was a veteran of 30 years rural experience, 'We uses this tool to help an animal get a move on, like when it needs a final reminder to exert one last big effort out of mud or a farm pit.'

He paused, rather relishing my interest in this unusual piece of fire service rescue gear, and smilingly went on.

'I know you're going to tell me you won't find this pepper pot in the Fire Service Drill Book or the brigade inventory, but I can tell you it has a magic effect when applied carefully up the rear end of a beast. Especially when it has my hot pepper mixture in it!'

And even if I didn't believe this story at the time, I surely did some few months later when I actually saw this fiendish device applied to a recalcitrant steer with very great effect!

Probably the most dramatic personal brush I ever had with animals occured during my earlier London service. My crew from Paddington fire station had responded to a '999' call to flooding in a luxury block of flats in Bayswater. The '999' call had been made by a patrolling PC.

He had been first called to the block when a flat occupier on the third floor noticed water dripping through his ceiling. The PC was unable to raise the occupier of the fourth floor flat above, but was able to see through its letter box that water was seeping from under a closed door within the flat. He had then called for fire service assistance and supposing the very worst, feared that the occupier might have collapsed whilst taking a bath, and duly asked my crew to force an entry into the flat.

Our wheeled escape ladder was quickly pitched to an outside window, inside which shone a light. My Leading Fireman ascended the ladder, peered in and then came back down. He reported that he could just see over the drawn curtains that the bath taps were running, although his view was restricted by condensation.

I quickly debated whether to attempt an entry through the closed window off the ladder, or to spring open the flat front door and deciding that the latter would be the most satisfactory method, took all our breaking-in tools up to the fourth floor, accompanied by the PC. As the front door to the flat was being somewhat noisily forced open, the elderly lady tenant of an adjacent flat appeared and in an alarmed voice asked: 'What's going on?'

With diplomatic aplomb, I assured the grey haired old lady that there was nothing to worry about although it must have appeared to her that some awful catastrophe had occured. A Woman PC had now turned up and she attempted to calm the lady when the aged tenant turned towards us all quite suddenly and said: 'I shouldn't go in if I were you – there's a snake there!'

At this point, the door to the flat had just been forced open and gripping the handle tightly to keep it pulled shut, I heard this information and inwardly my senses screamed. The PC behind me was ashen white, for he too had registered the dramatic news of a serpent within. The WPC was nowhere to be seen at all!

Then, with the door of the flat still firmly closed, I questioned the old lady neighbour who was adamant that the girl occupier of this flat kept a snake. There followed a deeply traumatic experience as I gingerly entered the flat, the deep carpet already soggy with water under my feet. With the hall light on, there was no snake so far, nor any sign of the girl occupier. Down the hall was the closed bathroom door with water still seeping out underneath; the light inside was still on and a towel was lying along the bottom of the door.

Very carefully, I edged it open. There, coiled around the swamped bathroom floor was the biggest snake I had ever seen – ten feet long and a foot in circumference at least. I slammed the door shut and turned around to my crew behind in the hall – from the looks on their faces, I did not have to explain the problem. They must have espied some of the slippery reptile through the open door. I also heard the muttered rumbling of the PC as he rapidly retreated into the corridor outside the flat.

Registering that I had still not looked into the bathroom long enough to check if the lady occupier of this strange flat was inside, and bolstered by the fact that I was under the critical gaze of my men, I gently opened the door once again to have a better look inside.

'Good God!' I cried out as I peered around the door. 'There're three of them in here!'

And there were. One, the first I had seen, was even longer than I had first estimated and the other two were both about six foot in length. All looked exceedingly unfriendly over the intrusion. There was certainly no girl in the bathroom but there was a hot tap running, two sun lamps glaring away and an article of laundry, no doubt dislodged by the snakes' movement, blocking the bath plughole and causing the overflow. Thankfully, I shut the door once more.

There followed a very stealthy search of the remainder of the flat and all then started to make sense. We found several photographs of a near naked blonde with snakes coiled around her body. The girl occupier was obviously a club stripper who used the reptiles as part of her act and normally left her 'pets' in the humid atmosphere of the bathroom.

Our appliance radio was now alive with messages as I asked Control for the urgent attendance of a vet, zoo keeper, the RSPCA, snake charmers or anyone who could identify and occupy the frightening creatures so that the hot tap could be turned off and the bath unblocked. Water was still running through into more flats on the third floor below. The PC returned to the scene looking even more shaken than when he left us; he told me that he had summoned his Inspector and that the 'nick' were also trying to trace the female charmer who owned the snakes.

In their search of the rest of the flat, two of my crew had discovered a large wickerwork basket in the lounge. It appeared to contain something alive within, for it was jerking and creaking. Using a steel hydrant-bar, the lid of the basket was lifted an inch or two and there was a baby rabbit inside. We breathed again! What part of the girl's act the rabbit consisted of, I knew not, but there was the thought that the helpless creature might be the next meal for the snakes.

Soon after, the police Inspector arrived and I fully explained the situation and that we were waiting for experienced help. After some deliberation, the Inspector said that if I held the bathroom door open for him, he would go in amongst the reptiles and turn off the offending tap. Despite my suggestion that it would be safer to wait for advice and perhaps let knowledgeable handlers take over the situation, he went ahead and stepped in over the snakes whilst I secured his means of escape. Three forked tongues flashed angrily at the Inspector as he reached across and turned off the tap. We then beat a hasty retreat out into the hall and the door was shut on the snakes, who by this time were becoming very angry.

The flooding below was then finally dealt with and the three snakes left secured in their tropically heated bathroom. We left the very brave Inspector to sort out the aftermath of the skirmish and to calm the somewhat nervous occupiers of the rest of the flats.

I subsequently learnt that the three snakes were all reticulated pythons, which normally crush their prey. Someone on my watch said he had read that a python could swallow a whole pig. Having seen the biggest of the trio at close quarters, I quite believed him. I mused too on the thought of what fate would have befallen my Leading Fireman if I had actually sent him into the bathroom through the outside window from the escape ladder. It really didn't bear thinking about.

Sometimes, an animal rescue can turn out to be other than it first seems. Such was the case which involved a crew of firefighters from Malpas fire station in Gwent Fire Brigade.

One four man crew had been despatched to deal with a rubbish fire on open ground and having extinguished the small pile of timber and paper, the firemen began to make up their hosereel and prepared to leave the scene.

As usual, the appearance of a fire engine and its crew

drew a small crowd hoping for some excitement. Out of this gathering came one of the local residents clutching a pair of binoculars. Addressing the Leading Fireman in charge, he said 'Excuse me, mate, but if it's of any interest, I've been watching a cow for the past ten minutes at Caerleon, and the poor animal has wandered down the river's edge and fallen on its back in the mud!'

He pointed to a suitable point from which the Leading Fireman could see the unfortunate beast. By then, it was beginning to get dark and the far off river bank was difficult to see clearly, even with the aid of binoculars. However, the location of the animal could just be determined on the river bank in the distance. This was about a mile away as the crow flies but over three miles by road.

The Leading Fireman returned to the Pump and reported the facts by radio to Fire Control, who then confirmed that the crew were to proceed to the animal in distress. Control also stated that a Rescue Tender, which was carrying animal slings and harnesses, was being sent from Malpas fire station to rendezvous with the Pump at the river bank.

Some ten minutes or so later, the Pump crew booked in attendance by radio as near to the river bank as they could get. Leaving the fire engine and its driver on the roadside they started to make their way across the field, full of long grass, towards the river. They were about halfway across the field when the crew caught sight of the blue flashing beacons of the Rescue Tender on the far side of the river, and the Leading Fireman told one of his firefighters to go back to the road behind them and guide the other fire engine into grassy field.

This was quickly organised and the Rescue Tender soon hove into sight and paused alongside the Pump. As the Rescue Tender driver prepared to carefully take his fire engine across the field to where the cow was reported stuck, he noticed the form of a firefighter looming out of the darkness towards the two fire engines. He came up to the Leading Fireman in charge of the Rescue Tender with his hands on his hips and spluttered breathlessly: 'That's one hell of a long trudge! But we don't need any of your animal rescue gear.'

'Oh, is it dead then?' enquired the Leading Fireman, rather relieved at not having to unstow all the special equipment on a dark and muddy river bank.

The tired fireman smiled but said nothing. By this time, a small crowd of residents had formed around the two fire engines and they watched with interest as he climbed up into one of the cabs and picked up the radio handset.

'From 312 at Home Farm, Caerleon. Cow stuck in river bank. Mistaken identity. 312 over.'

The female voice in Fire Control came loudly over the radio as the operator repeated the message, and then after a pause asked 'What was mistaken for a cow, over?'

Up in the fire engine cab, the firefighter held the radio mouthpiece close to his face and cupped his hand around the handset, and went on.

'From 312. An upside down armchair exposed by the low tide, over!'

There must have been some mirth back in the Control Room, because there was quite a pause before the radio crackled into life again.

'312, all received, I will not repeat but message noted. Out'

From the tone of her voice, the operator in Control was obviously having a job to prevent herself laughing out aloud over the radio. And as both crews prepared to leave the scene of the unusual false alarm, there were plenty of smiles, and not a little rudery aimed at the well intentioned resident who had sent the fire brigade to the so called cow in distress in the first place.

8
Smiling Through

Some of my most amusing experiences as a firefighter took place during my service in central London, although the work of the fire service everywhere is always spiced with the rich variety of life and its personalities.

One of my fondest memories as a young fireman is being one of a crew called to 'persons shut in lift' at a West End gentlemen's club in the early hours. Such 'special service' lift calls were not unusual in the West End, but upon our arrival at this emergency it was clear from the outset that this was not going to be an ordinary lift job.

For there, inside the lattice gates of the lift car, stuck about five feet below the proper floor level, was Tommy Cooper along with several other dinner-jacketed club members. They roared with laughter as we approached laden down with the usual tools needed to effect such a rescue, as well as two-way radios.

'Here they are,' Tommy called out, 'the bloody cavalry to the rescue!'

As the lift had stuck below the floor level, the comedian's head and those of the others trapped with him were about even with our feet, and as we looked down on the group inside the car Tommy, ever displaying the silly grin and large ears for which he was famed, started to regail his rescuers with various fireman stories.

To this day I cannot recall any of them. But I remember well that whilst others in the crew went up to the lift motor room in the roof space to isolate the electrical power, and prepared to release the brakes and hand wind the lift car to the floor below, the two of us left with the comedian quickly became part of his act.

It was hilarious. He tried unsuccessfully to make coins

disappear and then spent some time wrapping a set of keys in a white handkerchief, all the time ad-libbing and wise-cracking through his well rehearsed lines. Then there was a superb impression of Rob Wilton's Edwardian fire chief deliberating on whether to attend a fire call. Tommy asked me if he could speak into our radio and I passed the handset down to him through the lattice gates. More Rob Wilton impressions were sent up to my colleagues above as well as a slightly out of tune rendition of 'why are we waiting'.

It was magical stuff and neither my crew mate nor I could stop the tears rolling down our cheeks. It seemed a shame when, after about five minutes, the lift car suddenly jerked upwards inch by inch as the crew high up in the motor room started the delicate hand winding operation. Undaunted, Tommy kept going with several more abortive tricks and a ceaseless flow of jokes and banter until, after several minutes, the lift car was level with the floor and, having recovered the radio, I called up that the car and floor levels were now synchronised.

We were then able to trip the sliding door mechanism and Tommy and his friends emerged with warm handshakes and smiles.

'Well done, lads,' said Tommy, 'that was a damn fine job! Come and let me say thanks properly.'

Once the rest of the crew rejoined us at our level, he insisted that we followed him. The comedian trooped us all into the plush leather bar area. In deference to the surroundings all five of us took off our fire helmets, but felt very conspicuous amongst the black tie throng. Apparently there had been a gala boxing event earlier on.

Tommy pushed us all up to the bar and ordered beers all round. Taking our Sub Officer's helmet, the comedian raised it aloft and called out for some quiet. A hush fell over the crowded bar as Tommy Cooper called out, in a serious tone, 'Gentlemen – I give you the London Fire Brigade – God bless them and all who sail in her!'

We could not linger long, indeed nor should we have

done, but it would have been impossible to have escaped without Tommy expressing his appreciation of our efforts. And when, some little time later, Tommy Cooper sadly died on a London stage during a show, I thought of that very natural funny man who enlivened one emergency call in his own inimitable manner.

Fire service driving duties in the West End of London could also provide the occasional smile in some way or other. Not long after I qualified to drive Turntable Ladders, I was at the wheel of Manchester Square's new AEC/Merryweather 100ft Turntable Ladder (TL) going to a fire call at offices in Piccadilly, on Soho fire station's ground.

It was late morning rush hour, about 1000 hours, and the traffic was particularly thick going down the one way section of New Bond Street. In an effort to squeeze past the slow moving cars, buses and taxis, at one stage I eased the offside wheels of the long twelve ton fire engine up onto the pavement for a very short distance.

By the time I got the TL to the Piccadilly address, the small fire in an electrical junction box had been extinguished by Soho firefighters and I took the TL back to Manchester Square via Park Lane and Oxford Street at a far more serene and sedate pace.

Upon my return I was in for a shock, for I was summoned by the Station Officer who told me that a New Bond Street shop had reported that a fire engine had been involved in an accident outside the shop and failed to stop. I was staggered by this and quite unaware of any such accident.

What transpired was this. When I had put the TL's offside wheels up on the New Bond Street pavement, the weight of the vehicle had split an old cast iron coal cellar cover. This would not have been too serious had it not been right outside a New Bond Street couturier who just happened to have 'By Royal Appointment' displayed above the shop doorway.

I was dispatched forthwith in my best walking out uniform to the shop where a large wooden board was covering up my *faux pas*. Once inside, I had to personally apologise to the shop owner for the damage caused. She received my explanation without any expression apart from a nod of her head to dismiss me from the premises.

Subsequently I was found to have caused the 'accident' and felt rather peeved to have it recorded as such on my driving log.

Not long after this incident came a 'true' accident involving Manchester Square's fire engines. Early one evening shift all three appliances, Pump Escape, Pump and Turntable Ladder had been ordered by Fire Control to a fire in Rex Place, a narrow Mayfair back street just off Park Lane. I was driving the Pump, the second fire engine in the noisy procession, with the Turntable Ladder close behind. The Pump Escape led the way through the busy evening traffic. Both Pump Escape and Pump were recently commissioned new Dennis fire engines and had only been 'on the run' for about a month.

Out across Oxford Street, past Selfridges, then around Grosvenor Square, past the American Embassy and into the narrow back streets we went, finally swinging right into Rex Place. In the gathering darkness, there about 100 yards on the left hand side, was a smoke haze and just the briefest glimpse of orange flame at an upper window of the residential flats which lined both sides of the street. A working job was awaiting us.

By now the Pump Escape was down to about 5mph as its driver, Jim, carefully squeezed the first eight feet wide Dennis between the lines of parked cars on either side of the narrow street. Most were expensive models such as Rolls Royces, Bentleys, Jaguars and the like. At the wheel of the Pump, I cautiously followed the Pump Escape slowly up the street. There hardly looked room enough for any of us to get through to the unknown fire situation ahead.

The Station Officer on my left had his head out of this nearside window, and in the rear cab each crew member likewise were leaning out watching the tight clearances between the shiny new red paint of our fire engines and lines of luxury limosines on each side.

'Go on! You're OK,' they called. Then, 'Steady. Left hand slightly! Keep going,' as I glanced from mirror to mirror and eased forward after the Pump Escape in bottom gear. In my mirrors, I could see the headlights of the Turntable Ladder behind, driven by Alec. This fire engine was the same width as the two Dennis pumps, but rather longer.

About half way up towards the fire we sighted several people in the middle of the street ahead, frantically waving to us outside the burning flat. Fire was now very evident at an upstairs window. It was just then in the light of my headlights, that I thought I saw a few shining silver fragments flying through the air as the Pump Escape passed perilously close to a Rolls on the fire engine's offside.

'Keep going!' ordered the Station Officer, concious of the old adage that for a firefighter to be successful, he must take his equipment as close to the outbreak as possible.

The gap in front between the lines of parked cars through which the Pump Escape had now gone through looked even narrower. I went on at a *very* slow speed. Taking a deep breath and gripping the steering wheel very tightly, I braced myself for the impact that must surely come. But to my intense surprise, there was no bump or sound of metal on metal.

The Pump Escape ahead had now halted outside the burning flat. Its crew was already leaping about, pulling off the high pressure hose reel tubing, whilst our Sub Officer was already making a reconnaissance. Once I had stopped the Pump close behind, it was comforting to see the Turntable Ladder had also negotiated the hazards of the parked limosines. The three Manchester Square fire engines were in action together.

Once the three crews took two hose reel tubings through the flat front door and up the winding staircase to the first floor, the fairly severe fire in the bedroom was quickly knocked down, although the breathing apparatus wearers at the front edge of the attack took quite a lot of punishment in the intense heat, smoke and humidity. Fortunately, there were no fire casualties or injuries and we had contained the fire and prevented it breaking out up the staircase to the flats above. The owner of the flat and his wife were visibly shocked and distressed as we went about the clearing up and careful salvage operation amid the charred remains of their possessions, all the time looking for clues to the cause of the outbreak.

Whilst this work was going on, I and the two other drivers found time to walk around our respective fire engines to locate any bodywork damage as a result of squeezing between the parked cars all down the narrow street.

To my particular relief, my new Dennis appeared unscathed. However, as I walked back to the Turntable Ladder behind, both Alec and Jim were stooped down on the TL nearside. Both drivers had long faces which told their own story.

The Pump Escape driven by Jim appeared to have made contact on its nearside with a parked car, whilst the TL had a similar long indentation on its mid offside.

'What about you?' they both asked quizically.

Smugly, I replied: 'As clean as a whistle!' and unable to resist a further response to the two senior drivers of the watch went on: 'It's about time you chaps learnt to judge your distances!'

Their replies if I recall properly were quite unprintable before both Alec and Jim, with torches in hand, went back down the street in search of the parked cars with which they had both made contact.

About an hour later, when all three crews had returned to Manchester Square fire station, the report writing started. Fortuitously, the third party damage was confined to two car wing mirrors, even if in true Battle of Britain style, the Pump Escape had got a Rolls whilst the Turntable Ladder claimed a Jaguar.

Serious accidents involving fire engines are thankfully rare, especially bearing in mind their size and today's traffic levels. Nowadays, there is an even greater emphasis on driver training and safety. But the call that night to Rex Place and my unblemished passage through the tightest of gaps, did a lot to restore my personal pride and standing after the saga of the New Bond Street manhole cover, and the subsequent leg pulling I had endured.

Another illustration of the varied hazards in driving fire engines in London's West End existed right outside Manchester Square fire station situated in narrow Chiltern Street, just off Oxford Street. Directly opposite the three fire engine bays stood a long row of small terraced shops. One of these was a greengrocers, and such were the tight clearances between the front of the Turntable Ladder when it turned out and its front overhang of eight feet or so, and the greengrocers sun blind, that a special drill was evolved.

When a '999' call was coming in, one firefighter was detailed to dash over to the greengrocers so that he could grab a pole and quickly push the sunblind back into its housing. If, as so often happened, the greengrocer was serving a customer, the pole was kept in a strategic location just inside the shop so that we could push the blind in ourselves, thus allowing the TL to swing out of the fire station opposite and head off safely to the '999' address with only inches to spare! All this action took place in about thirty seconds or so, and many shoppers stopping off for a pound of tomatoes or a cauliflower had little idea of the importance of the strange ritual with the pole enacted as the fire bells rang out in the fire station opposite.

Quite often, a fire service driver has to react and be alert for sudden changing traffic circumstances, well illustrated by an incident which occured whilst I was a supervisory officer in the West End. At this stage of my career, I had graduated to a staff car and although this should

have been less hectic than riding fire engines, it was anything but.

Apart from negotiating the dense traffic congestion
between fire and other '999' calls, there was the navigation
to contend with in an area which stretched from Kings
Cross to Notting Hill, and from Kilburn down to
Westminster. Then there was a constant stream of radio
messages from Fire Control at Wembley, who handled all
the incoming '999' calls for the inner London zone, and
many of these were prefixed with my call sign as the West
End was a very busy operational area. Although the staff
car, a white Austin 2200, was fitted with blue flashing
beacon and two tone horns, ploughing a path through the
West End traffic could be a nightmare.

About 1000 hours one miserable, drizzly London morn,
I was just leaving Knightsbridge fire station after a routine
visit when my call sign came over the radio ordering me
to proceed to a reported fire in Duke Street, St. James.
Quickly registering that my most direct route was along
Knightsbridge to Hyde Park Corner, and straight through
the underpass into Piccadilly and the St. James district, I
switched on the blue beacon, headlights and two tone
horns, and started to move down the outside of the traffic
queues ahead.

After three or four minutes of traffic weaving, I came
up to the approach to Hyde Park Corner where the buses,
taxis, lorries and cars hardly seemed to be moving for the
congestion all around. As I slowed up, there close by a
traffic island ahead, were two motorcycle policemen sitting astride their white BMW's. As I came alongside one
of the mobile PC's prodded his mount into gear and eased
alongside me, the drizzle dripping off his open helmet
visor.

'Where are you going to, Chief?' he called out over the
throbbing exhausts of the BMW.

His motorcycle smelt very hot and rain droplets sizzled
on the exhaust pipes as both my radio and his police set
competed noisily for attention.

'Duke Street,' I shouted through my open window over the combined noise of radios, motorcycle and traffic din. 'Duke Street, *St. James!*'

Before I could be sure he had fully heard my qualified address, the PC opened the throttle of his motorcycle and waved me to follow him up the outside of the traffic lanes. The obliging policeman moved forward gesticulating vigorously to the traffic queue to move over as he sought to carve a path for my fire car.

As we slowly approached the large underpass and roundabout that is Hyde Park Corner with its statues and war memorials, I began to wonder if the police motorcyclist had properly heard my destination. For he had started to swing left towards the Park Lane exit and not down through the underpass which was my original intended route to the fire call.

In truth, there are two 'Duke Streets' in London's West End, one not far ahead from where I now was, off Piccadilly on the far side of the underpass. The other Duke Street lay about a mile away off Oxford Street and the shopping centre to the north up Park Lane. The St. James suffix told one from the other.

As the motorcyclist PC continued to bear left into the Park Lane exit, still waving all the traffic over and clearly heading for the Oxford Street 'Duke Street'. I had no option but to proceed into the underpass straight ahead in order to reach the correct address. The PC obviously had not seen our paths diverging, for he was now about 100 yards ahead amid the Park Lane traffic queue, still frantically standing up on his footrests, moving slowly forward waving the buses, taxis and cars over.

Then he was out of sight as I went down into the underpass, easing the Austin staff car down the outside of the slow moving line of vehicles, the blue flashing light reflecting off the tiled walls whilst the two tone horns raucously told of my urgent approach.

Within a minute or so, I was out into the rain again and signalling to turn right off Piccadilly and its traffic throng into Duke Street, St. James. There at the bottom of the street, were three fire engines and their crews getting to work amid a heavy smoke haze, tackling a serious fire in a basement storeroom below a tailors shop.

After an hour or so of hard physical work in breathing apparatus, firefighters from Soho and Manchester Square had the fire under control. As they began to clear up I walked up the street to my staff car, fully expecting to see the police motorcyclist demanding to know where the heck I had got to. But strange to say, he never appeared and for some days I half expected to come upon the white BMW and its bemused police rider roaming the West End looking for a missing London Fire Brigade staff car!

Firefighters who serve on inner city fire stations get called to the most amazingly varied non-fire emergencies and human misfortunes. Sometimes these are the direct result of the demon drink as the following story well illustrates.

During my time as a junior officer in the London Fire Brigade, I would occasionally be in charge of one of the Brigade's Emergency Tenders. These were travelling workshops which carried much specialist rescue and cutting gear. Emergency Tenders were despatched to all '999' calls such as road crashes, machinery accidents and the like.

One summer evening, a call (or shout in firefighters' slang) took the Paddington Tender to Victoria Embankment Gardens, close by Charing Cross Pier, where it had been reported that a man had fallen onto some railings and was injured.

By the time we arrived with the Emergency Tender, the firemen from the local station, Soho, along with an ambulance crew, were already supporting the casualty who was quite conscious and apparently perched on top of the railings, with an ornamental spike well and truly embedded in his buttocks.

My crew very quickly got two air-operated metal cutting saws to work to cut off the top of the offending railing spike. However, this had to be done most carefully in order to disturb the wound as little as possible. Fortunately, the poor fellow was not bleeding too much.

The plan was that we would cut through the spike, then remove the casualty and small section of railing to hospital to allow its final removal under proper surgical conditions.

Whilst the cutting operation was under way, the injured man who was obviously Irish, seemed relatively unpeturbed by his predicament. Indeed, he even managed a smile and showed remarkably little outward pain to his rescuers. This may have been sheer bravado on his part but was more likely to do with the very high level of beery fumes which were emanating from the chap. In somewhat staccato phrases and in between incoherent bursts of singing, the Irishman told us that he had just been taking a short cut over the railings when he slipped.

Happily, after some ten minutes careful cutting, he was at least free from his immediate plight, although there must have been about ten pounds of metal still attached to him as he was carried into the waiting ambulance. We then started to clear up all our equipment when the young doctor of the medical team which came to the scene during the later stages of the rescue asked if the Emergency Tender could follow the ambulance to nearby St. Thomas's Hospital to be on hand should any further metal cutting be required.

Once at the hospital, my crew hurriedly conveyed quite a lot of equipment into the casualty suite in case it was needed. Needless to say, the sight of six firemen hurrying to and from their fire engine parked outside caused quite a stir amongst both hospital staff and waiting casualty patients alike.

In the event, our skills were not needed as I watched the casualty team remove the spike without too much difficulty whilst the Irishman remained none the worse for his adventure. Paradoxically, it was a fair bet that his boozy state which caused the accident also eased his suffering. I wondered if the brewers of that famous black Irish beverage had ever considered its value as an anaesthetic!

If there was any sadness at the conclusion of this unusual emergency it was that before we left St. Thomas's, I discovered that the casualty doctor had claimed the ten inch metal spike for the hospital's 'black museum'. This was a great shame as I had designs on it for our fire station collection!

The old army story of 'send reinforcements, we are going to advance' becoming distorted into 'send 3/6d, we are going to a dance!' took on a new meaning for me soon after I had been promoted Station Officer in charge of a watch (or shift) of London firefighters.

During the rush hour one winter morning, my crew had dashed to answer a '999' fire call to smoke coming from an empty office complex alongside Paddington railway terminus, off Praed Street. Because of the traffic holdups the first of the three fire engines, the Pump Escape with my Sub Officer in charge, had arrived at the railway station ahead of the Pump, with me on board, and the Turntable Ladder close behind.

The outcome of this was that my Sub Officer and his crew reconnoitred the upper floors of the empty complex for several minutes before I arrived, and they quickly found a small smouldering pile of timber, probably where a vagrant had slept during the night. Two buckets of water were all that was needed, and my Sub Officer then sent word down a staircase to the street below to appraise me of the situation upon my delayed arrival.

Unfortunately, as the Pump Escape crew dealt unspectacularly with the small fire, the Sub Officer's message which started off as: 'Tell the Guv'nor it's on the fourth floor' had been progressively relayed and transposed to eventually become 'Make Pumps 4.'

This was a standard priority radio message asking for immediate and urgent further assistance at the scene of a spreading fire. As I drew up on the Pump outside the building, the Pump Escape driver was actually sending this priority assistance request over the radio to Wembley Control.

Sorting all this out took a little time, especially as the district supervisory officer was automatically sent to any 'Make Pumps 4' call and more. He was very quickly on the scene, as were two other Pumps from Knightsbridge and Kensington fire stations, all wondering how it was that Paddington firefighters had put the fire out so speedily without their help.

Outside the capital, firefighters in the shire counties have their fair share of unusual and humourous incidents. During my service in West Sussex, one very rare occurence took place in the village of Partridge Green where the brigade had a one Pump retained/volunteer fire station located.

Such rural fire stations exist throughout the United Kingdom where the fire risk is such as to not demand a full time fire crew. A small number of suitable local men and women are recruited and trained to man the fire engine in event of an emergency. To do this, during the daytime they have to be able to leave their normal job or profession immediately when their bleeper signals them into action. Although such retained fire stations do not answer large numbers of fire calls, they do occasionally have to deal with serious and dangerous incidents just as effectively as their professional city colleagues do.

On this occasion, the officer in charge of Partridge Green, a butcher by trade, arrived to open up his shop early one morning. It was located just opposite the fire station, and he noticed that the large red doors were open revealing that the Partridge Green crew were out on a call. He was rather puzzled by this as his own bleeper had not sounded, so he walked into the fire station to see just where the crew had been sent.

Stranger still, the teleprinter showed no mobilising address and the butcher then rang Fire Control at Chichester.

'Partridge Green here,' he said. 'Where has the crew gone?'

There was a pause at the other end as the Control Operator surveyed the large mobilising map of the county and its various fire stations.

'Well,' she replied rather cautiously, 'Partridge Green haven't been turned out this morning. We are showing them in the station!'

The butcher averted his gaze into the adjacent empty fire engine bay and its open doors.

'I'll ring you back shortly,' he went on, 'I think we've got a problem!'

And so it was that after he had made a few rapid enquiries around his crew at their places of work, it became clear that someone had got into the fire station during the night and stolen the Partridge Green fire engine. The police instigated an immediate search of the area whilst my staff organised a spare fire engine to provide fire cover for the district.

After an hour or so, the missing Dennis fire engine was found parked in a disused quarry. Apart from being rather muddy, it appeared undamaged with all its firefighting equipment intact. The subsequent police enquiry eventually led to a prosecution of a youth who had apparently taken the fire engine as a means to getting home. The replacement cost of a new Dennis Pump at that time was about £70,000 with as much again going on its equipment. No wonder that all concerned with this unusual theft felt a sigh of relief when the missing fire engine turned up unscathed.

Another amusing West Sussex '999' call which was not what it seemed took Horsham firefighters to a call to a van on fire. When they arrived they found that the 'smoke' coming from the vehicle was nothing more sinister than innocuous vapour clouds coming from a defective onboard refrigeration system. The van's cargo included a quantity of animal sperm destined for some Sussex farms and the precious liquid had to be kept chilled during its journey. This was one predicament when the fire service could offer little real help.

Of all the humourous incidents that I have been involved in or am aware of, let me conclude with a brief story of a London Fire Brigade Turntable Ladder (TL) crew going noisily to a fire call down The Mall towards Trafalgar Square one summer morning.

As they approached Clarence House, the London home of the Queen Mother, there was the Royal Rolls Royce with its standard flying on the roof coming out onto the junction with The Mall, preceeded by an unmarked police escort. Traffic in the Mall ahead of the fire engine was coming to a halt as police officers prepared a path for the Royal car. Despite this, the Leading Fireman in charge of the TL rang the bell loudly and kept the two tones going as the fire engine driver slowed up on their approach to the Clarence House junction, both firefighters acutely aware of the Royal personage ahead.

But their dilemma was immediately resolved as a police constable stepped out into the Mall some 100 yards ahead of them, and waved the fire engine down the outside of the traffic queue ahead. The TL driver swung the twelve ton fire engine down the outside of the halted traffic line and past the Queen Mother waiting to proceed on her way to her morning engagement.

As the two firefighters swept past, they both just momentarily raised their fire helmets deferentially at the Queen Mother. And back at Paddington fire station afterwards, they were quite certain that the Queen Mum had waved back at them as the Turntable Ladder passed by on the day the London Fire Brigade took precedence over the much loved elder member of the Royal Family.

9
Plenty of Pathos

It is true to say that whilst a firefighter does find quite a lot to laugh about in the course of operational duty, fire crews are by the very nature of their work witnesses to many tragic, sad and often pathetic scenes.

Thus it was that a fairly ordinary sounding '999' fire call in Harley Street, W1, just after dawn one very cold January morning, turned out to be rather more than my crew had expected.

As our fire engine turned into Harley Street, there ahead was a sizeable smoke haze and a lone police constable waving to us in the middle of the deserted and frosty roadway.

'There's a fire in the coal store!' the young policeman called out as we screeched to a halt and pulled off the hosereel tubing.

'In the basement coal store, under the pavement,' he went on pointing down into the smoke to the stone steps which led down into a small basement area.

Each of the substantial houses in this 'medical' centre of London's West End had such an under-pavement coal store. This was fed from a circular iron cover in the pavement, although most had long since been disused as fuel stores.

I quickly led the crew down the stone steps to the basement area. The smoke did not seem too thick, more like that from a pungent bonfire and appeared to be coming from inside the coal store itself.

Checking quickly that our high pressure hosereel water was ready, I gently opened the door into the coal store and in so doing, released huge clouds of bottled up smoke which forced us to lie down flat. The coal store was only about four feet square inside and as the hosereel was sprayed around to clear some of the acrid smoke, floodlights and a breathing apparatus crew arrived to ease the task. As the white light bathed the scene, it became obvious that what was burning inside the coal store was a small and unthreatening pile of firewood.

But, as the breathing apparatus crew clambered inside the store amid the smoke to extinguish the burning timber, they suddenly encountered a sack like bundle behind the coal store door. Reaching down to check, the firefighters quickly realised that the bundle was an unconcious human form.

In a few seconds, the breathing apparatus clad firefighters had pulled the person out of the smoke from where the casualty was rapidly carried to up to the pavement level above.

He was still alive at that stage, a smoke blackened London tramp, but despite our resuscitation efforts, the scruffily clad vagrant died before the ambulance crew got him to the nearby Middlesex Hospital.

Once we had put the small fire out and ventilated the coal store, it became evident that the tramp had been living in the otherwise empty sixteen square foot coal hole for some time. There were a few 'personal' effects, such as some moth eaten blankets, an enamel mug, a pile of dog-eared glossy magazines, several candles, and quite a few empty wine bottles.

The low temperature had no doubt led the tramp to light a fire which had contributed to his lonely death by asphyxiation, in Harley Street of all places, during that cold and frosty London winter dawn.

Another encounter with a very much alive vagrant took place not very long after the Harley Street fatality. We had been called from Manchester Square fire station to assist the police in gaining entry to a rather run down and partially empty block of flats in the back streets close to Marylebone railway station.

A vagrant had barricaded himself inside the second

floor flat, in which apparently he had been 'resident' for some considerable time. The fire service role at this incident was simply to provide a ladder to allow police officers access into the flat, so that they could question the tramp regarding several local petty thefts.

It all appeared fairly straightforward until the moment came that we had taken a ladder off the Pump, and were just extending and pitching the ladder top into the second floor window when a bearded, long haired and grimy face appeared at the window.

'Bugger off, you sods!' yelled the occupant of the flat. The vagrant was obviously much the worse for drink as he swayed at the window opening and tried unsuccessfully to push the top of the ladder away from the building.

Then he disappeared momentarily, only to appear again this time brandishing a wine bottle which he then hurled down right alongside me. Jagged fragments of green glass bounced on the pavement all around.

'Clear off. Sod off!' he continued in a slurred yet noisy tone.

There was another pause of a minute or so as both policemen and firefighters took shelter behind the Pump in expectation of another missile from above. However, after five minutes or so had passed there were no further wine bottles, or indeed, any sign of the tramp.

After a brief consultation with the police inspector present, he decided to ascend our ladder with a police constable and gain entry into the flat via the window. The incident was, after all, still a police matter.

But just as the two policemen prepared to climb the ladder, I noticed an almost imperceptible wisp of smoke drifting out of the open window above, and inside thirty seconds or so, it was clear to all that there was now a fire starting to develop inside the building.

Now no longer was this just an 'assist police' call, as I quickly issued instructions for two of my crew to don breathing apparatus whilst directing the remaining two firefighters to pull a hosereel tubing off the Pump. Suddenly, we were thrust into the front line, and the smoke was thickening at the window by the second.

'You up there, stand clear!' I shouted upwards. 'This is the fire brigade and we are coming up and in!'

And with a brief word with the police inspector who assured us he would not be far behind, up I went with one of my crew. Between the two of us, we manhandled the weight of a hosereel tubing up to the open window where we were enveloped in fairly thick smoke. With streaming eyes, we both went in through the open window, but not before I had checked with my hands and feet that all was safe inside. Once inside, we lay flat, pulled in the tubing and took gulps of the warm yet near smoke free air layer always found an inch or so from the floor in a burning room.

There was, as far as we could see into the rolling smoke, no sign of the angry occupant. All I could determine was a single dim unshaded light bulb glowing in the murk and then being aware of being close to high stacks of carrier bags, bulging plastic sacks and piles of rolled up newspapers. An orange glow was showing over the far side of the room and despite the biting tang of smoke so familiar to firefighters, there was an awful nauseating smell seemingly all around the two of us.

By then my two breathing apparatus clad crew had climbed in through the window to relieve us, and taking the hosereel forward into the piles of jumble they set off to extinguish what was a small yet already deep seated fire, presumably lit by the tramp. This allowed the two of us to rapidly retreat from the smoke and fumes onto a landing, where the police inspector and several PC's had assembled.

'It'll soon be under control,' I gasped. 'It looks like he's lit a small fire in some rubbish and old newspapers and then cleared off. I don't think he's in there.'

Right on cue, one of my firefighting team put his head around the corner of the door onto the landing, causing some smoke to come wafting out of the flat.

'It's out, Guv, and all the windows are open,' said my Leading Fireman, his breathing mask dangling around his neck to reveal a sweating and reddish face. 'Only a few old newspapers burnt, but we do have a slight problem.'

'Go on,' I said, half expecting a wisecrack from one of my crew who would normally never miss an opportunity to raise a laugh.

'Well, Guv,' said the Leading Fireman as he started to explain, at the same time grimacing slightly. 'It's the bundles of newspapers, both those charred by the fire and those that are not. It looks as if he's crapped in every one of them at some stage, and then just rolled 'em neatly up!'

It was an awful scenario to behold and the Leading Fireman's face said it all. The two breathing apparatus clad firefighters had made their foul discovery as they started to damp down the rolls of stacked newspapers, and had only then dawned on them that the vagrant must have been defecating into the newspapers. It quite belied belief as there was a lavatory out on the landing.

There is a standard ventilation procedure used by firefighters after a fire in a building, in which the maximum through draft is encouraged via windows and doors to clear the smoke and steam, and to induce cool air into the hot structure. On this occasion, ventilation was also needed to clear the stench of the fetid newspapers, especially after they had been disturbed by the firefighting operations.

The police never did discover where the tramp took off to after the fire and this incident really was a classic example of a '999' call that ended up very differently to how it had started out.

My Leading Fireman summed it all up somewhat laconically after we had all had a much needed shower back at the fire station.

'Well, I don't know how long that guy's been squatting in that flat but judging from the piles of newspaper, I'd say it wasn't yesterday!'

But soon after this somewhat smelly and unpleasant

incident came a fire tragedy of enormous proportions which affected the lives of quite a few firefighters in the London Fire Brigade, especially me.

Harry Pettit was a probationer fireman in the London Fire Brigade. He was in his mid twenties, and married with an eighteen month old son. Harry had always harboured a desire to be a firefighter and after completion of the three months recruit course, he was posted to one of London's busiest fire stations, at Paddington where I was the watch commander. Sadly he was not destined to enjoy a long and fulfilling career. For some six months later, Harry died in dramatic circumstances at a fire at the Worsley Hotel, Maida Vale on a fateful Friday 13th.

On this date, Harry was one of 200 strong force of firefighters who on an icy cold and dark early morning had pitched ladders to carry out multiple rescues, then ran out hose and donned breathing sets to tackle London's largest fire of that year.

To Harry and the rest of us on the 33-strong Red Watch at Paddington, it started as many large fires do. The swirling smoke, drifting sparks and fleetingly, a glimpse of fiery flame at the upper windows with the melee of fleeing residents, some almost naked, added to the chaos and confusion that met us as Paddington's fire engines drew up outside the Worsley Hotel. And because we were the first firefighters to arrive, there was a certain parochialism in those first hectic minutes. Upon our actions and decisions depended the lives of those still inside the building, not least those many residents trapped above the fire and screaming out for help on the roof and at upper floor windows.

In all some 36 men and women were rescued from these perilous ledges and windows, mostly by Paddington firemen, including Harry. By then, more fire engines and their crews were arriving thick and fast from fire stations all over central London to support the intense firefighting and rescue effort.

After about an hour, as the fire was finally being surrounded on all sides and coming under the first signs of control, part of the fire-weakened roof suddenly fell in. This collapse overloaded the floor below, which in turn crumbled like a pack of cards down into a second floor area where a team of firefighters was working. Harry was one of this team.

The rescue effort to dig him and the three others out of the hot and compacted debris was a race against time. Only a few rescuers could get into the space left between the unsupported walls, as friend dug for friend with frantic and superhuman effort. That whole end wall of the hotel was now quite unstable and to further complicate the situation, the fire was still burning very close at hand.

After almost three hours of desperate work in the most dangerous and difficult conditions, three of the entombed firemen were finally released, each badly burned. Tragically, rescue for Harry was just too late. He had been buried the deepest under the hot brickwork and glowing timbers.

The firefighting had carried on as far as possible during the protracted rescues and word soon filtered around the scene that although three firemen had been extricated, the fourth was dead. A number of firemen from Paddington had not been able to take part in these rescues although all had earlier volunteered to go into the hell-hole on the second floor where the firefighters lay buried. As dawn finally broke over the still smoking and blackened frontage of the Worsley Hotel, it was pretty clear to the local crews by simple elimination just who had given his life some hours earlier. Not a few Paddington firemen had clean streaks made by tears on their grimy and weary faces as they were progressively relieved by fresh crews from all over the capital.

Within an hour, Harry's wife had been located at work in North Kent and gently told personally by a London Fire Brigade officer of the tragedy. By midday, early planning was already in hand for a full brigade funeral with all its panoply.

As the Station Officer in charge of the Red Watch at Paddington, one of my responsibilities during the daytime after the fire was to collect Harry's personal belongings. These included not only uniform and civilian clothing, but items of sports gear as well. The professional closeness and teamwork of the Red Watch had long spilt over into many such off duty activities, and Harry like the other newer recruits on the Watch, had flung himself into soccer, rugby and volleyball with great gusto.

Choosing my moment in the late afternoon with great care, for the fire station was still working under the Blue Watch, I stood alone in the spacious empty dormitory on the first floor and turned the key of Harry's locker. Inside its door, I was confronted with a colour photograph of small laughing child being held aloft by Harry on some happy occasion. I spent twenty minutes or so neatly packing Harry's locker contents together, and put the photograph carefully in an envelope on top of the folded clothing and other items. This sad and moving task over, I prepared for the parade and roll call of Red Watch who were shortly due on duty for their second night stint of fifteen hours.

At 1800 hours, the Red Watch had fallen in in two long lines in the fire engine bays with their backs against the four gleaming red appliances, each with their cab doors open awaiting the first '999' call of the night. The Watch were rigged in clean and dry firefighting uniforms and stood immaculate, motionless and very silent.

I nodded to my Sub Officer beside me in front of the parade to begin to call the roll and detail the crews and other duties of the shift. He held the roll call and duty board upon which there was now a conspicuous space on the alphabetical list of Red Watch personnel.

The crisp command 'Attention!' echoed across the fire engine bays, bringing with it a smart and simultaneous crunch of fireboots on the tiled floor, and there was just an slight pause before the first name was called out. As I proudly surveyed the two rows of firemen, many of whom were very experienced and hardened veterans of past battles against fire both won and lost, I saw that tears were again falling for Harry and his loss.

On the run up to Harry Pettit's funeral, which was due to take place a week after the fire itself and only a few days before Christmas, I could not help recalling another large London fire service funeral some five years earlier in July 1969. This followed the deaths of five London firemen and a civilian following an explosion in a derelict oil tank at Dudgeon's Wharf, in Millwall, East London.

One of the firefighters who was killed, Trevor Carvosso, had been a good friend of mine who, only two weeks before the fatal explosion, had along with me been representing the London Fire Brigade in an inter-fire service athletics match. Trevor was a gifted sprinter and long jumper.

At the full fire brigade funeral for the five firemen killed in the Dudgeon's Wharf explosion, there was a huge turnout of uniformed London firefighters who lined the route through the streets of Stratford, East London, where the funeral service was conducted.

Before the commencement of the service and the arrival of the cortege, I was placed in the guard of honour close to the entrance of the church. It was a quietly impressive scene with a single file of firefighters on either side of the long approach path up to the church. Not only were there hundreds of London firemen present to pay tribute to their five fallen colleagues, but the numbers were swollen by representatives from virtually every British fire brigade. The guard of honour thus stretched away on either side of the main road from the church as far as the eye could see. Everywhere were brushed serge fire tunics and caps, highly polished webbing belts and shoes, and immaculately creased trousers. Many firefighters were wearing their medals for what was a 'state occasion'.

After about fifteen minutes, the lone command came for the guard of honour to come to attention as the first of the five gleaming Turntable Ladders, each carrying an individual coffin arrived outside the church. The silence was all pervading as each group of six capless and white-gloved pall bearers drawn from each dead fireman's watch, took the weight of a coffin, turned slowly and with carefully synchronised steps, headed up the path into the church. Each coffin was draped with the Union Jack, and was topped with each firefighter's helmet, together with several of the more personal of the hundreds of floral tributes.

Opposite me in the facing line of the guard of honour were several firemen from my own fire station, Manchester Square, and as I sensed the approach of the first coffin from my left hand side, the awful loss of an entire fire crew in one explosion suddenly took hold of my emotions.

The first two coffins were borne reverently and slowly past my position into the church entrance, but there seemed to be some sudden momentary hold up, for the third coffin and its bearers paused for some fifteen seconds or so right in front of me before moving on. My eyes were first transfixed upon the bearers, each of whose tear-stained expression and dignity told of their personal suffering and loss in the tragedy, and then to the coffin itself. I could see from the wreaths and the engraved brass plate that this was the coffin of Fireman Trevor Carvosso.

A fortnight back, he and I had been competing against firemen from other fire brigades and now he lay dead in a coffin right in front of my gaze, killed as he went about his work as a London firefighter.

As preparations for Harry Pettit's funeral after the Worsley Hotel fire drama gathered pace, I again remembered Trevor Carvosso and all those before him who had given their lives in the most noble duty that a firefighter can perform.

Pathos is never really far from the work of the fire service although it can embrace a firefighter in all manner of ways. Imagine the sights and suffering which regularly confront fire crews, be it a fire situation or an accident scene. No firefighter can hope to remain unaffected by it all, although there is the compensating closeness of working as part of a team, as well all the detailed training and preparation for those moments when the difference between life and death can be measured in seconds.

Such as the springtime day when I was crewing Paddington's Emergency Tender which responded to a '999' call to 'a child trapped in a lift' in a hotel in London's Edgware Road.

On being met and told by the distressed porter that the child was trapped in the lift at third floor landing level, my crew, armed with toolboxes and first aid kit, vaulted up the highly imposing marble staircase that wound around the lift shaft and its steelwork.

As we approached the third floor landing, the Sub Officer in charge of our crew detached one of our number to console a near hysterical woman, clearly a foreigner, who transpired to be the child's mother.

Of the child, all we could see through the small glazed lift door panel was a leg pushed hard against the window. Sadly there appeared no sign of any movement.

Apparently the child, a boy, was holidaying with his parents at the hotel and whilst playing in the corridor, had opened up the outer door to the lift and then reached through the inner lattice gate of the lift car proper. Somehow, the lift call mechanism had actuated and the lift car started to ascend to the upper floors. The unfortunate child was then picked up by the ascending lift car until he became jammed between the car and lift shaft. As that happened, the impact physically tripped the lift winding mechanism and the outer door had then slammed shut.

The problem was simply how we could quickly get into the lift shaft to rescue the child. To open the outer door, which we could easily do by way of special door-trip mechanism keys, would possibly cause the boy to fall down the lift shaft into the basement, four floors below.

A plan was rapidly evolved and as another crew joined us with more specialist rescue gear, the lift shaft door on the floor below was opened. Another fireman and myself then placed short ladders out into the shaft underneath the lift car in order to provide a base from which to work above.

Once we were perched precariously out in the shaft, now brightly lit by powerful lighting from off the Emergency Tender, the lower part of the poor child's body was visible only a few feet above me. I was quite sure at this stage that he could not have survived the crushing impact of being drawn upwards. Other firemen had opened the fourth floor lift shaft door above the lift car and there was now no doubt that the child was already dead.

Yet another crew had gone up to the lift motor room on the roof of the building, isolated the electrical power to the lift and were now ready to lower the lift car manually, using hand winding equipment.

My delicate task was now to grasp and support the child's body as the lift was gently inched down to a position where the crew at third floor level could open that door and remove the body to safety.

A medical team consisting of a doctor and two nurses had also arrived but were clearly not going to be needed. Several policemen had also turned up and led the weeping mother away from the scene.

Several minutes later we had the child out and as I momentarily took the boy's weight, and gently passed the floppy and lifeless form out of the shaft to my colleagues on the landing I thought, as most firefighters do at such times, of my own child. Very briefly, every fireman present grieved for both the victim and family of yet another human tragedy that had claimed a young and innocent life, before trying to concentrate on clearing up all the various items of rescue equipment we had used in the rescue attempt.

These types of difficult rescues demand a special teamwork from all those taking part, whether firefighters, police or ambulance personnel. This is never more so than during the extrication of a person who has fallen under a London underground train as it has entered a station.

Such casualties are mostly the outcome of a suicide attempt and generally suffer fatal injuries.

On these occasions, despite emergency braking by the driver, the train passes over the casualty by about half its length of six carriages before coming to a halt. After being struck by the train, the person underneath is likely to have fallen into the three foot deep pit between the running rails and the two live power rails.

Firefighters will then have to ensure that the train is braked and its wheels chocked before isolating the electrical supply to the power rails. Only then can they drop down into the pit and wriggle back under several carriages to locate the hapless person. Then, with the assistance of railway engineers, the train will be carefully parted to allow full access to the casualty by the rescue crews, often with a hospital medical team in support.

At best, the casualty will still be alive yet seriously injured from the impact of the train or from electric shock and burns. At worst, fire crews will have the job of collecting various parts of a dismembered body from the pit beneath the running rails and putting them into plastic bags for the coroner's officer. The pits opposite the platforms in London underground stations are not the cleanest areas of the railway system at the best of times, and to have to crawl through one to recover parts of a body must be one of the most unpleasant tasks a firefighter ever has to perform. I know, for I have had to do it several times during my time in central London.

People who are trapped above a developing fire in a building naturally tend to hang out of open windows screaming for rescue. Some even climb out onto narrow ledges to escape the rising smoke and heat from the fire below which has cut off their normal escape route. At worst, they will actually jump, often to their death from multiple injuries after plummeting down onto the pavement or roadway below.

Indeed, the priority task of the first firefighting crew at such a potential fire scene is to prevent 'jumpers' by shouting out to them to: 'Hang on! We're coming up to get you!'

But even as ladders are pulled off the fire engines and into action, the unexpected can and does happen.

A crew from Kensington fire station had gone to a daytime '999' fire call at a hotel in Earls Court and as they turned the corner into the street concerned, there from a second floor window was a huge red and orange fireball rolling out fire and smoke. Above, on a ledge at third floor level, was a lone and cowering man, fully dressed and about thirty years of age. He was clearly threatened by the severe fire below, and the Kensington firemen set about their task.

Frantically calling up to the trapped man not to jump, the wheeled escape ladder was crashed off the fire engine, turned and rapidly wound up to its fifty foot height, then pushed in to touch the front of the hotel. A protective water jet was aimed at the growing flames and with more calls to the man to 'Stay there!', he seemed to understand and even waved back to the firemen in brief acknowledgement that rescue was very close at hand.

Then the Leading Fireman of the crew was on the escape and literally running up the ladder, close to the flames and through a torrent of cooling water now being aimed at protecting him from the scorching radiated heat of the fire. Dripping wet, the firefighter arrived at the ladder top, and with the trapped man almost within touching distance alongside him on the ledge.

Just as the Leading Fireman reached out to offer a steadying hand onto the escape ladder, the trapped male suddenly jumped off the ledge, fell through the flames below to crash sickenly into the basement area fifty feet below. There were screams and loud gasps from the sizeable crowd that had gathered to watch the drama, and sadly the poor chap was obviously dead by the time the nearest firefighter got to him.

Just why he jumped, when rescue was so very close, was never established at the subsequent inquest although there was some evidence to suggest that he had started the fire in the hotel bedroom himself. He had checked into the hotel alone and had very little possessions with him. It was all very strange and very sad.

An even more tragic example of a 'jumper' fatality came soon after the Kensington hotel fire death and involved a serious nightime fire which took place in Montagu Place, in London's Marble Arch district. It involved a four storey block of flats.

By the time the first fire crew arrived, two people, a man and a woman, were screaming out for rescue from a small balcony on the top floor, amid the swirling smoke from the fire below them. Despite a frantic and dangerous rescue attempt by several firefighters using a Turntable Ladder, the woman could not wait and jumped. Fortunately, her companion was snatched to safety just as a flashover occured in the bedroom alongside the balcony. The rolling ball of flame blew out the glass frame of a window and scorched both rescuer and rescued, although both survived.

I was the duty supervisory officer in the West End that night, and despite it being bitterly cold and frosty, was soon on the scene with firefighting operations by then well in hand. The Turntable Ladder was still elevated into the night sky as the live casualties, including Fireman Montgomerie, were being put into the ambulance.

Right in front of the smoking building, on the pavement was a blanketed and still form. As I approached there were wisps of golden blond hair showing out from underneath, in stark contrast to the scarlet red of the ambulance blanket which draped the dead young woman just where she had fallen. A ambulance crew were preparing to remove her body once she had been formally certified dead by a doctor.

She had a beautiful face, quite unmarked in her fall, although it was evident that she had suffered fatal injuries to her back. I recall she was wearing what appeared to be a pink silk dressing gown, and although this was now damp from the water all around from the firefighting jets, she looked at complete peace despite the sudden and traumatic end to her young life. Her features seemed intensified by harsh floodlighting which had now lit up the entire area like some outdoor theatre stage set.

One of the firemen of the first crew on the scene had been very close to the spot on the pavement where the woman had fallen. He was a probationer, only three weeks out of training school.

'She crashed down, right on top of the fire hydrant, just as I was going to connect up!' he said very quietly after I had called him over during the clearing-up operation.

'This your first fatal?' I enquired.

'Yes, Guv', he replied, 'and I hope they are not all like this, are they?' he asked earnestly, as he stared me in the face.

I paused for a moment or two, as we both looked down at the still form on the wet and frosty pavement as the doctor completed his necessary examination, and thought of all the many fatalities I had seen and been involved in during my years.

'No', I replied. 'Every fire or accident death you deal with will be different, because it's a different set of men, women and children involved every time.'

I hoped that my reply had not sounded too trite to the new recruit, and that he had taken in the adage that had in turn been passed down to me when I was a young probationer fireman.

Incidentally, some months later, Fireman Montgomerie was awarded the Queen's Gallantry Medal for his rescue efforts on that cold and frosty tragic London night.

Two other incidents which readily highlight the sort of human suffering seen by fire crews were both the result of road traffic accidents (or RTA's in the parlance of the emergency services).

The first of these took place during the time I was a Divisional Commander in West Sussex Fire Brigade. Crews from Horsham fire station had been called by the police to a road crash on the A281, a mile or so out of the town one wet autumn evening. When they got to the accident site, they found a small Ford van had left the road at a sharp bend and hit a large tree head on.

The van occupants were a young couple and a very tiny new born baby. The father, who was driving the van, was badly trapped by the compacted front end of the vehicle, which in turn had crushed both his feet around the pedals. He also had some serious chest injuries caused by the steering wheel being pushed back into him.

Fortuitiously, the mother had escaped with only a bump on the head and even more miraculous was that her baby, which had been in the back of the van in a restrained carry cot, also appeared unharmed. But the struggle to get her semi-concious husband out turned into a difficult and trying exercise. She wanted to be close to him as we set to work to cut him free, and she stood by the side of the crumpled van, cuddling the baby and gently cradling him up and down as we worked from both sides, and from the front to free the trapped driver. She steadfastly refused to move away from the wrecked van despite all our persuasions.

We had made significant progress in prising over the gearbox assembly, cutting through the steering column and part of the side bodywork by the time a hospital team arrived. One of the nurses immediately tried to get the young mother to sit down in one of the ambulances now at the scene. Thankfully she agreed to this as delayed shock began to set in, but only on the condition that she remained at the scene. The doctor reluctantly conceded to this and then gave his full attention to stabilising the medical condition of the driver, as we worked on with the extrication rescue.

Within fifteen minutes of further intense teamwork on the reluctant bodywork of the van, the husband was finally free and gently lifted out onto a stretcher, a drip already in place. The doctor appeared satisfied that there was no immediate threat to the driver's life.

As he was carefully placed into the waiting ambulance, the nurse transfered the young wife still clinging to her baby into the same vehicle, to be reunited with her husband. As the ambulance crew started to close the rear door, I glimpsed that the injured driver was sufficiently concious to cling tightly to his wife's one free hand as she squatted down alongside the stretcher, a family reunited after their ordeal.

The final recollection of pathos and the firefighter involved me at a much more recent RTA, not long before my retirement from the service as Chief Fire Officer of Devon. My staff officer, Rod, and I were proceeding in uniform by car to a meeting in Wiltshire, and were heading along the A303 trunk road not far from Stonehenge, when we came upon a traffic queue going towards a long left hand bend ahead. Just visible in the distance were two large goods vehicles, both at strange angles to each other, and Rod switched our blue beacon and headlights on, and cautiously drove down the outside of the traffic queue.

And there some two hundred yards down the carriageway was an awful crash scene that had clearly only just taken place. Two articulated trucks had rammed each other, both going in our direction, but their drivers were both out and being tended to. Two cars were also seriously involved and in one of these, an Austin Maxi, the driver still appeared to be slumped behind the wheel.

Rod quickly parked my fire car up on the grass verge and sent an urgent radio message over the inter-brigade channel for all three emergency services, whilst I ran over to the Maxi to see if the driver could be got out. The car was half up on the verge and at right angles to the A303. It had one entire front half completely stoved in. The woman driver, a lady in her sixties, was very badly trapped, covered in shattered glass from the windscreen and appeared to be lapsing into unconciousness. Several other casualties from the other vehicles were either lying down on the grass or stumbling around.

But there was little I could do for the poor woman,

except to comfort her as best I could, although when Rod
came running over to confirm that help was on the way,
I got him to disconnect the Maxi's battery which was
completely exposed on one side at the car's undamaged
side. He had also brought my car's fire extinguisher with
him as the thought of fire breaking out did not bear
thinking about.

There did not appear to be anyone else in a serious
condition amongst those casualties around the accident
site, and it was very helpful when a young woman came
over, saying she was a nurse and asked if she could be of
help. I asked her to stay with the trapped elderly lady
driver to ensure that if at all possible, her airway was
kept free. Only later did I discover that the nurse herself
had been a passenger in one of the several other cars
involved in the multiple shunt.

Then a uniformed RAF officer ran over to see if he too
could be of assistance, and he quickly started to dress
several of the bleeding wounds of those sitting on the
grass verge, whilst I tried to establish if there was anyone
who had been a passenger in the Maxi.

Throughout all this time, which seemed to be twenty
minutes or so but in fact was much less, I yearned to hear
the two tone horns of the emergency services approaching
the accident scene. Both Rod and I felt so wretchedly
helpless with no power or hand cutting tools at our dis-
posal to free the badly injured woman. Unfortunately, the
RTA had occurred in a fairly remote spot out on the edge
of Salisbury Plain.

After a little time we located the Maxi driver's husband
sitting propped up against a gateway. He had a deep gash
on his forehead and repeatedly asked where his wife was.
I reassured him that all would be well but wanted, if at
all possible, to keep him from seeing his wife's plight.
However, in his state of shock he was pretty confused
and appeared content to stay sitting where he was.

'What's your wife's name?' I asked as gently as I could.
Thankfully, in the distance could be heard the very

welcome sound of two tones of the first units of professional aid fast closing on the accident site. Another
helper was trying to dress the husband's head wound and
staunch the blood flow, and I had to repeat my question.
He looked at me with a weary yet almost knowing look
before replying: 'Dorothy. It's Dorothy.'

With due haste, I hurried back to the Maxi where both
the nurse and Rod were still tending the trapped female.
The nurse gently held the driver's head off the jagged
metal edges of the door frame, whilst Rod held dressings
on serious injuries to both her nose and scalp. I bent down
very close to the trapped woman and spoke as slowly as
I could into her ear.

'Dorothy...Dorothy, can you hear me?'

She seemed to stir slightly and her eyes opened momentarily.

'Dorothy, we're going to have you out of here very
soon, You're going to be alright. Your husband is fine.'

Then Dorothy's head seemed to flop forward before
the nurse adjusted her supporting grip, as we both looked
anxiously down the A303 to see the headlights and blue
beacons of the first fire engine on the scene with a police
car in close pursuit.

That first fire engine, from Wiltshire Fire Brigade's
Tisbury fire station, drew up right alongside the wrecked
Maxi and the crew piled out and started to unload their
cutting and lifting gear. Their Sub Officer came running
over to me to appraise the situation. Seeing my shirt sleeve
rank markings, he respectfully asked if the lady driver
was the only trapped casualty, and then took a rapid look
at how she was pinned in the crushed Maxi. By that time
his crew had all the cutting gear ready to go, and as the
second Wiltshire fire engine also arrived together with an
ambulance, it was time for Rod, myself and the nurse to
step back and let the Wiltshire crews get on with the
rescue effort now unfolding. For by now I was very late
for my meeting still some ten miles or so further on down
the A303, and when it was appropriate, we slipped away

from the scene after leaving our names and contact numbers with a police officer who was beginning to collate all the accident details. As we eased off down the A303 in a London bound direction, it was evident that the Wiltshire fire crews had got Dorothy out of the tangled wreckage of the Maxi.

Much later that evening, and back at my headquarters in Devon, I rang my Wiltshire opposite number, John Craig, to pay my own tribute to the professional skill and careful work of the various Wiltshire firefighters during the extrication operation on the A303 that morning.

Sadly, he told me that the woman driver had not survived the crash. As I bade him goodnight and put the telephone down, my mind went back to that part of the A303, the Maxi and to my few words with Dorothy.

It had been quite a few years since I was regularly first on the scene at RTA's, but even a Chief Fire Officer can readily recall earlier training, experience and disciplines in order to deal with serious road crash situations. However, to come across a trapped driver as Rod and I did that fateful morning, without the benefit of modern cutting and spreading tools, was not an experience either of us wanted to go through again.

Sections of the busy A303 near to Stonehenge remain fast and at times hazardous stretches of road, and every time I nowadays drive past the spot where that accident occurred, I remember my few words to Dorothy in the hope that she at least knew and understood that skilled and caring help was very close at hand.

10
Crashes and Chemicals

A growing number of today's '999' calls to the fire service involve non-fire emergencies, or 'special service' calls as they are termed. Such calls were quite a rarity up to the Second World War, but have now grown to become a large part of a fire brigade's workload.

In many cases, as many as 25% of the calls answered by firefighters can be to 'special services' and in fact Her Majesty's Chief Inspector of Fire Services reported that fire brigades in England and Wales turned out to over 190,000 individual non-fire incidents in 1990. Add those dealt with by Scottish firefighters and the total number of these calls is in excess a quarter of a million!

The range of special service calls is almost endless, and can be leakages of dangerously toxic chemicals to the horrors of road crashes with drivers and passengers trapped. Flooding after sudden prolonged rainfall, gas explosions and persons trapped in machinery accidents can and do tax the courage, inginuity and skills of fire-fighters, as can the occasional serious rail or air crash. Some of the problems of the rescues of animals and children in various predicaments are set out in earlier chapters, although whilst lift rescues are commonplace, one involving a famous comedian such as Tommy Cooper is perhaps less so!

Road crashes however do predominate amongst non-fire calls, which is little wonder given the massive growth, speed and density of modern day traffic. Unfortunately, it is not uncommon for fire to break out after motorway and other high speed crashes in which fuel lines become severed.

The worst motorway road crash in the United Kingdom

happened on 21 October 1985 on the M6 in Lancashire.
A small fire quickly started and was fed from leaking fuel
amid the wreckage and added to the horror of the scene.

The first '999' call to Lancashire County Fire Brigade
Control came at 1322 hours just as fire crews at the nearest
fire station to the accident, Fulwood, were grabbing a
quick lunch. The Sub Officer approaching the scene on
the first fire engine graphically describes the nightmare
awaiting his crew:

'*I can hardly describe the sight that confronted us.
There was a line of vehicles, including a coach, stretching
from one side of the carriageway to the other, virtually
all of them ablaze; the embankment was covered with
people, many of them injured. Some were lying on the
ground, some just staring numbly at the devastation in
front of them.....At 1337 hours, I asked for further assistance by radio.....my message said there were many casualties and possibly ten dead. I prayed I was over estimating
the number of deaths.....As more pumps arrived, we
quickly got the fires under control.....There was a total of
twelve vehicles involved. We searched them all and found
two persons dead in a car at the rear of the crash area.
Mercifully, there were only three fatalities inside the coach
but, sadly, when we finally managed to open up two cars
that had been flattened against the front of the coach, we
found two children and two adults in each. This was a
very distressing discovery for us all and brought the final
death toll to thirteen.*'

Another more recent serious motorway crash which
gave great difficulties to the fire service took place on 13
March 1991 on the M4 in Berkshire. On a densely foggy
morning during the commuting peak hour, 40 cars and
light vehicles and three heavy goods vehicles collided, and
impacted into one solid mass of tangled metal. Fire soon
broke out amid the wreckage, again fed from quantities
of spilt and leaking fuel.

There were many problems facing the Berkshire firefighters right from the outset, apart from the thick fog

hampering their speedy arrival. In addition, the police received four conflicting '999' locations of the accident given by mobile telephone users. When fire crews finally arrived at the burning vehicles strewn all down one carriageway, they were confronted by simultaneous tasks of the rescue of many trapped motorists and passengers, as well as firefighting with limited supplies of water. The final toll in this awful crash was ten dead and 25 serious hospital casualties.

One nasty crash I will always remember, if only because the fire engine I was in charge of was itself involved in an accident en route to a '999' call. The Pump was moving fairly fast down towards Queensway in London's Bayswater district very late on a drizzly winter's evening, in response to a fire alarm sounding in a Kensington office block. Keith, the driver of the Pump, started to ease up for a series of traffic lights we had to cross. All of them were showing us a green aspect, and there was little traffic about except for several headlights coming in the opposite direction.

Keith slowed the Pump down in anticipation of the first green aspect changing to amber, and concious also of the greasy wet road, kept our road speed down to about 30 miles per hour as we went through the first set of traffic lights, still showing green. It was then that we both noticed one of the vehicles approaching us from the opposite direction about a hundred yards off, suddenly veer into our path. Its headlights were coming straight at us on our side of the road. Through the rain-smeared windscreen it looked like a large saloon car.

'Oh, no!' cried Keith, 'He's gonna hit us!'

As he stood on the Pump's brakes, a head on collision was inevitable as Keith had no escape route to take the fire engine.

'Hang on!' was all I had time to call out to the three firefighters in the rear crew cab and braced both my legs for the crunch.

The car, a large silver Mercedes, hit us square on at

about 20 miles per hour, and the impact shook the fire engine to a jolting halt as bits flew off both vehicles in a clattering cascade of metal, glass and plastic.

Keith said he was alright but was obviously shaken as we got out. There were ominous loud groans from inside the rear cab. The Dennis fire engine had pushed the Mercedes back about ten feet and both vehicles were enveloped in clouds of steam from the two punctured radiators. As Keith helped the crew out of the rear cab, I went to see how the maniac car driver had fared.

He was still sitting behind the wheel of the Mercedes, groaning loudly and nursing a smashed and bleeding knee-cap where he had been thrown forward by the crash. His door was badly crumpled and unopenable. He appeared to be Asian, and as he looked at me in my full firefighting kit, he cried out what sounded like: 'Ceedee! Ceedee!' repeatedly. As he was not seriously injured, I decided to leave him where he was until the police arrived.

The rest of my crew sat on the pavement nursing their bumps and bruises after being thrown around the rear cab. One had a broken tooth and plenty of blood coming from several cuts to the forehead. I asked on the radio for some urgent assistance; both police and ambulance as well as two more fire engines, and all this help was soon at the scene.

The fire crews cut the driver's door off the Mercedes and were then able to wriggle the injured Asian out after the ambulance crew had dressed his smashed knee. My wounded crew were also taken off to hospital for a check-up although I declined, having come out of the collision apparently unscathed. This was more than could be said for our Dennis Pump. The entire lower front end was smashed in with considerable damage to the cooling system, steering and engine block. It was a lift and tow job.

As for the Asian driver, the Mercedes was displaying CD diplomatic plates as an embassy car and I realised that its driver must have been claiming immunity of some sort. When, many months later, the case came to a magistrates court as a case of dangerous driving, Keith and I were called to give evidence. Neither of us was surprised when it was confirmed that the Asian had earlier 'left' the country rather than face the consequences of British law.

Interestingly, fire engine drivers are required to obey the road traffic laws as are all road users, with the exception that whilst proceeding to a '999' call they may exceed the speed limit. Fire engine drivers must also obey traffic light signals, although they are permitted to cross these at red if they have first stopped and are absolutely clear that all other road users are aware of the fire engine's intentions. In event of an accident in which the firefighter driver is found to be at fault, he must then face the legal consequences, the same as any other road user. Today's fire service driver training has a strong safety awareness input, for few drivers can surely be under such duress and pressure as those at the wheel of a fire engine, en route to an '999' call.

But outside Marlebone Magistrates Court that morning, both Keith and I felt very aggrieved that the miscreant foreign driver had vanished after clearly being responsible for a crash which, bad though it was, could have had fatal results.

Apart from the perpetual number of road traffic accidents, vehicles do sometimes contribute to some unusual special services. Like the exploding refuse lorry in a backstreet just off London's Marble Arch.

Making their routine calls to shop and office premises, the refuse collectors picked up several bottles, drums, rubbish cartons and other paper packages from a recently vacated building and all these items were tossed into the lorry and pushed forward by a compressing device. Unknown to the operatives the empty premises had last housed an industrial chemist's, and as a second load of boxes was thrown into the vehicle, a loud explosion from within the lorry knocked several nearby refuse collectors flat on their faces, started a fire inside their vehicle and rattled all the windows down the street. The fire in the lorry was still burning fiercely when the brigade arrived several minutes later and the injured men were speedily removed to hospital.

As the firefighters dealt with the fire, it became apparent that amongst the boxes inside the dustcart were many containing assorted chemicals which had interacted to produce an explosive cocktail. The fire call quickly became a 'chemical' incident.

Police evacuated the street whilst fire crews in protective clothing and breathing apparatus climbed into the refuse lorry and started to unload and sift through the five tons or so of rubbish already collected within for signs of any more 'lethal' rubbish. This unpleasant task was coordinated by the brigade's chemist who was now at the scene, and a full decontamination area was set up ready to deal with any fireman who made accidental skin contact with any suspect substance. After four hours of painstaking and gentle digging amid the rubbish by over fifty firefighters working in relays, all the many containers and packages of discarded chemicals were recovered, many intact, and the incident was finally closed.

Rail and air crashes are, like exploding refuse trucks, thankfully quite rare, but sadly do occur from time to time. The sheer destructive force of rail and air crashes is always an awful sight to behold, but railway collisions nowadays rarely tend to involve fire due to the all metal construction of modern rolling stock.

However, I have been part of rescue teams at several serious rail accidents, including that at West Ealing, a few miles outside Paddington in 1973. A London–Oxford rush hour service had got up to about 70 mph, when a defective battery box door on the locomotive fouled a set of points as it passed over. The diesel turned onto its side whilst the next six carriages zig-zagged across all four tracks. Most carriages turned onto their sides too, and a number of the 650 passengers on board were trapped for a time amid the crushed and tangled wreckage. Sadly, ten persons were killed and 94 seriously injured.

Another major rail crash rescue job for London fire-fighters took place at Eltham, in South London, some six months earlier. An excursion train returning to London from Margate came into a 20 mph curve at an estimated 65 mph, derailing the locomotive and the leading seven carriages, all of which were badly damaged. It was many hours before all the wreckage had been cleared of casualties by fire, ambulance and medical teams, and the tragic toll of this tragedy was six dead, including the train driver, and 126 injured.

My personal experience of air crashes include a large turbo-prop freighter which slewed off one of the runways at Heathrow in 1968 and hit several more modern jet aircraft, cleanly slicing their tailplanes off. The freighter was carrying racehorses back from an overseas meeting, and the wreckage and damage across a wide area was awesome.

In 1972 came the Staines British European Airways Trident disaster in which all 109 passengers and nine crew were killed when the aircraft came down in a field only minutes after take off from Heathrow.

More recent air accidents include the disaster at Manchester Airport in 1985 involving a fire on board a British Airways Boeing 737. Fire broke out in one engine as the aircraft was taxying, and before the pilot could halt the Boeing, fire had got into the fuselage. 55 passengers perished in the smoke, despite some heroic rescue efforts by the airport fire crews and firefighters from the Greater Manchester brigade. Miraculously 82 escaped to safety.

Then, in 1989, came the dramatic crash of a British Midlands Boeing 737 onto the M1 motorway at Kegworth, in Leicestershire, as it failed to reach nearby East Midlands Airport after an engine fire. The fuselage broke up into several large pieces on impact, and a huge rescue operation by firefighters from the Airport, and Leicestershire, Nottinghamshire and Derbyshire brigades was mounted. 79 survivors were eventually extricated from the wreckage, although 47 passengers lost their lives in the crash.

Leaking gas can also prove a major hazard to the community all around and when vast quantities are involved, the risks increase tremendously. Two incidents in my experience highlight this, and both involved propane, a commonplace liquefied petroleum gas (LPG) used for a wide range of heating processes. Under normal circumstances, LPG is stored as a compressed liquid in strong steel cylinders but when it is released, it quickly turns to a flammable and explosive gas.

The first of these LPG emergencies involved some very large storage tanks at a factory in West Sussex. About a hundred tons of liquid gas was under storage and during a prolonged spell of hot weather, several of the tank safety valves had opened as the internal gas pressure built up to a dangerous level. Plumes of white vapour hissing upwards into the sky quickly sounded the alarms and fire crews from several fire stations were soon at the scene.

The solution was to cool the tanks as quickly as possible to reduce the internal tank pressure and allow the valves to close. In the meantime, a very flammable cloud of gas drifted off downwind and police toured the area to evacuate residents and ensure, as far as possible, a 'no smoking' zone.

With copious supplies of water and the use of the inbuilt water spray fire protection system, firefighters eventually applied sufficient cooling water onto the huge tanks to allow the valves to close and the system to return to normal.

But LPG is a fuel that is readily transported and a more recent special service, this time in Devon, again illustrates the dangers that can be lurking everyday in our midst.

Late one winter afternoon on the Bristol bound carriageway of the M5 near Exeter, a tanker lorry laden with about nineteen tons of LPG crashed across the central reservation and overturned. Miraculously, it did not hit any vehicles coming in the other direction. Neither was there very much spillage as the tank body and its flammable cargo withstood the impact of the crash.

However, after the driver had been freed, the exercise to transfer the LPG load to another tanker was a tricky one, necessitating the closure of the M5 for many hours and the evacuation of a nearby village as a safety precaution. Firefighters worked closely with specialist teams from the LPG fuel company in a lengthy operation which carried a constant risk of fire and explosion.

The fire service thus has a great respect for liquid petroleum gas, particularly when these commonplace cylinders are involved in fire. Once heated up they can explode like a bomb, and project parts of their metal shells into lethal lumps of flying shrapnel.

One such incident in West Sussex showed all too clearly the explosive risk from these gas cylinders. One fire engine and crew had answered a nightime fire call to a builders shed on fire at a construction site. Sure enough, as the firefighters turned up the shed was, in their slang, 'Going like the clappers!'

But what they did not know was that inside the blazing shed were a number of gas cylinders. Just as the crew dismounted, one overheated cylinder suddenly exploded and showered burning fragments all around the site.

A jagged lump of metal struck the Sub Officer in the legs just as he got down from the fire engine. Such was its force, the cylinder fragment went right through the fire engine, punching a clean hole through its bodywork. The Sub Officer was seriously injured and subsequently lost part of one of his legs. Although his fire service career was abruptly ended by this dramatic incident, he was undoubtedly lucky to live to tell the tale of the exploding cylinder.

The explosive force of LPG ignition was well shown some years back at a Spanish camp site full of summertime holidaymakers. An overfilled and defective LPG tanker suddenly ruptured as it passed the campsite. A massive gas cloud spread all around driven by the wind and almost at once, the gas found a source of ignition. The fireball that followed was enormous and deadly. As it swept across the campsite it consumed all in its path, leaving a huge scorched area of blackened cars, caravans and grass. Over 100 men, women and children died a most horrible and sudden death as they enjoyed the Spanish sun on that dreadful day.

But it is the leakage and spillage of dangerous substances, whether in transit, in store, or in some industrial process which frequently present firefighters with considerable challenges. In fact, it was the steady growth of this type of emergency allied to the increasing use of dangerous substances, including acids, alkalis, oxidising agents and the like, which led to the first scheme to mark tankers and containers with a code pioneered and understood by the fire service. This scheme has since been superseded by more sophisticated marking regulations, which with the growth in international and national tanker traffic has become even more essential.

Consequently, it has become of paramount importance for firefighters to quickly know the safest method of containing and dealing with a chemical leak or a spill. Many liquids or powders will react explosively if water is applied, whilst others may be so toxic that spillages must be prevented from entering watercourses.

Alongside the development of marking schemes have come improved breathing apparatus sets and all-enclosing protective clothing, for some substances are dangerous to the point that the inhalation of only a few parts per million can be lethal. With the growth of such emergency calls, new routines to decontaminate firefighters who personally deal with the leak or spillage have also had to be evolved.

Of all the hundreds of various crashes I have attended during my fire service years, one stands out as the very worst scenario that could possibly be imagined – the Moorgate London Underground tragedy of 28 February 1975.

At the height of the London morning rush hour, at about 0846 hours, a six carriage tube train crowded with incoming commuters failed to slow down for its last stop at the Moorgate terminus on the Northern line, ploughed through the sand-drag and buffer stops and slammed into the wall inside the dead end of the tunnel. The front three carriages crumpled like a concertina, and in a few horrifying seconds many men and women were crushed to death. However, in the packed confines of the front carriages many commuters clung perilously to life despite serious injuries and being jammed into torturous positions, often beneath or alongside inert bodies. Upon the tremendous impact of the crash, all the lighting in the train and on the platform went out and the whole area was clouded in thick black dust, but fortunately no fire broke out.

When the first fire crews arrived soon after the crash, the enormous scale of the tragedy and the task ahead became clear, and their officer in charge initiated 'major accident procedure'. In accordance with the prearranged plan, fire appliances, ambulances and police cars were summoned from all over central London and nearby hospitals put on full alert.

Fortunately, the rear three carriages of the train were quickly cleared of blackened and dazed casualties and a mass assault was mounted to free the many people trapped in the front part of the train. The crushed and tangled red metalwork of the carriages seemed to fill the 70ft long dead-end tunnel and initially only one fireman at a time could wriggle into the wreck through holes cut in carriage end panels and roofs, or by worming a path up the narrow sides of the tunnel and into the train through the shattered windows.

As the firefighters crawled into the carriages, they saw in the light of their powerful torches that a number of people were already beyond help, although many others were trapped, injured but conscious. Many of the survivors said that once they saw the firemen coming through the wreckage towards them they knew they would get out alive.

All the fire service power cutting equipment, crowbars, hacksaws and many other tools had to be passed into the train by the same difficult path. As the morning wore on the live casualties were released one by one, and manhandled back down through the train and out to the platform where the ambulance service took them for the short journey to hospital. All the firemen were going into the wreckage stripped to the waist in the ever-deteriorating conditions. They worked under and amongst tons of hanging and mangled metal, slowly penetrating further and further into the mass. But progress remained excruciatingly slow.

A surgical team from a nearby hospital had earlier set up its equipment on the platform, and doctors frequently crawled into the wreckage to give drugs to a victim while firefighters worked on undaunted. By mid morning, twenty five trapped passengers had been extricated, although about forty were still pinned in the crumpled front two carriages. Floodlighting had now been provided inside the wreckage and on the platform and fresh relief crews took over from the grimy night shift of firemen still at the scene, as more and more fire engines arrived at Moorgate. By noon, seventy casualties had been removed, but heat continued to build up to add to the discomfort of those still trapped and their toiling rescuers. Working in temperatures of over 38 degrees Centigrade, the fire crews sweated away cutting, bending and lifting the twisted metal and timber of the carriages. Occasionally with a quiet and reassuring word, they comforted the passengers who were still trapped.

After many hours of grimy work, around mid-afternoon it became evident that only two of those still trapped in the train were alive. One of these, a young off duty policewoman, was hopelessly caught by her foot. Only after a valiant struggle to free her did the doctors decide that drastic steps must be taken. A crew of firefighters supported the woman whilst a surgical team amputated her foot at the ankle. She was then gently carried back through the carriages and an hour later the last live casualty, a young man, was finally released.

Then began the sad task of retrieving all the many bodies still entombed amid the wreckage. Over the next three days and nights, teams of firemen worked to recover them, while the air in the tunnel became progressively more fetid. All fire crews had to wear filtered masks and gloves as they struggled to free the crushed forms. Later still the atmosphere in that tunnel of death became so putrid that firemen had to don breathing apparatus and any direct contact with any body meant a full decontamination shower and a fresh set of clothes. The tiniest scratch necessitated an anti-tetanus injection, for the medical advisers present were growing increasingly worried about the health hazard to the rescue teams. By the fourth morning after the crash, all fire crews entering the train had first to change their own uniforms for dungarees and rubber boots that were then completely cleansed after a crew had been relieved.

As each piece of wreckage was finally cleared of bodies, it was winched out of the dead-end tunnel by railway engineers and the last and final body, that of the driver of the train, was recovered on the evening of 5 March.

Over 1,000 London firemen had been in attendance over the five days and four nights following the Moorgate crash and the final toll stood at 42 dead and 76 persons injured.

Many tributes were paid in the following days to the work of the London Fire Brigade in the rescue effort but the most apposite of these was probably that of London's Chief Fire Officer of that time, Joe Milner. He simply talked of, '*my 1,000 selfless heroes*'.

The Moorgate accident put an enormous additional burden upon the rescue teams, simply by virtue of the dead-end tunnel location of the crash. But many of the special service calls answered by the fire service take place in remote locations, and often during extreme weather conditions which both contrive to make already difficult situations even more trying for all concerned.

A good example of this kind of special service took place during the winter of 1988 in Devon during a very wild period of weather. In a remote country spot, not far from the village of Stokeinteignhead and in one corner of a steep and sloping field, lived a caravan dweller by the name of Walter. He had been a farm worker for most of his life but since his retirement had lived a quiet existence in and around his elderly caravan.

Then came the night of a prolonged thunderstorm accompanied by high winds and torrential rain. The storm had already been sufficient to loosen and bring down several large trees in the Chudleigh area, and as Walter tried to get some sleep, an ancient oak very close to where Walter's caravan was parked, started to sway and list dangerously towards his little home.

By the time the tree finally crashed over onto the caravan, Walter had dozed off, but the sudden and frightening noise of the buckling panels and splitting of wood woke him immediately. Walter found he was pinned down in his bed by the sheer weight of the tree trunk having fallen right across where he lay. The roof above his bed had gone and the rain and wind blew in around him as he lay there absolutely helpless, buried amid the broken timbers and aluminium panels of the crushed and partly disintegrated caravan. At least he was conscious even if completely unable to free himself.

Walter's rescue started several hours later, some time after dawn when the storm had subsided. A tractor driver passing down a narrow muddy track high up above the field, noticed the tree which had fallen right across Walter's caravan, and ran down to see if he could help. Although Walter was still concious he was by now suffering from shock and exposure, and the farm hand dashed off to raise the alarm.

Even then, it was some twelve minutes or so before the first fire engine appeared at the top of the hill, having come down the narrow track as far as it could. Then the crew and the following firefighters had to unload all their jacks, lifting kit, and cutting gear, and slip and slither down the wet slopes of the field towards the wreckage below. It was a veritable assault course, through a thorn hedge and then over several fences before they were able to kneel beside Walter, still pinned in his bed, to assure him that they would soon have him out.

It was first necessary to jack up and support the weight of the tree trunk as it was beginning to sink into the muddy ground and as it did so, it threatened to slowly crush Walter beneath its several ton bulk. This jacking operation was difficult in itself, as the individual jacks quickly sunk into the mire also. The answer was to rig a series of jacks with the weight of the tree spread over an area supported by several air filled cushions and bags. But all this took precious time throughout which Walter's condition deteriorated.

Fortunately, a medical team had also arrived to assist in the rescue and they decided to call in the Devon & Cornwall Police helicoptor. This aircraft was equipped to remove seriously injured accident casualties and was soon hovering over the scene, as the fire crews worked on jacking, propping and cutting into the crushed caravan. The helicoptor pilot landed the aircraft as close as he could nearby and after some very determined and careful work amid the wreckage, Walter was gently eased out of his erstwhile tomb. After some brief medical attention he was loaded carefully into the helicopter and, accompanied by the medical team, lifted off for the short journey to hospital in Exeter. It had taken over 3 hours to extricate him, and apart from severe shock and exposure, his only injuries were some cuts and bruises.

Clearing up and cleaning all the tools and kit used in the rescue operation took a great deal longer and it was some very weary, wet and muddy fire, ambulance and police personnel who staggered back up to their vehicles, long after Walter was warm and dry in hospital. Remarkably, he survived his long ordeal which suddenly began when his roof fell in on that wild and stormy Devon night.

As with firefighting, the key to success in crash rescue work is regular 'hands-on' training. This breeds confidence and teamwork when real life is at risk, and every second counts in getting a trapped and badly injured casualty out of crumpled wreckage. Another story shows just how well retained firefighters at a small county fire brigade station adopted an unusual approach to creating some realistic training.

Soon after my promotion and transfer to Bedfordshire County Brigade, I went to visit Biggleswade, one of the brigade's part time 'retained' fire stations during their weekly evening drill night.

However, upon my arrival I could see that the two fire engines based there were not in their bays. The lone firemen who greeted me explained that the crews were waiting for me at the site of a nearby historic aircraft collection at Old Warden.

Five minutes later I drove through the main entrance of the collection, and was directed by another waiting firefighter across the car park and out onto the grass runway. I then saw the two Biggleswade fire engines parked about 800 yards away on the far side of the airfield. The only other vehicle in sight was a rather battered looking dark blue Mini parked much nearer my position.

My curiosity was heightened as the Mini suddenly took off with a huge lurch amid a cloud of oily smoke, and headed down the runway towards me. Only then did I see that the two fire engines were also on the move as their blue beacons and headlight came on and their two tone horns started blaring out.

Still rather slow on the uptake, it then dawned on me that they were chasing the old banger which by now had got up to about 50 mph. Judging by the noise from its engine and its protesting suspension as it roared across the grass surface, the Mini must have been flat out.

Suddenly, as it neared me, it swerved violently off the runway path and came to an abrupt halt amid the long grass only fifty yards from where I was spectating. In no time at all, the two fire engines were upon the little car and its driver, who had now slumped unconcious over the wheel.

Biggleswade's shining red fire engines pulled up on either side of the Mini; the two crews soon had a powerful jet of foam going as well as a water spray and two firemen were operating dry powder extinguishers. This firefighting attack was directed all over and around the Mini. Within ten seconds, the creamy white bubbling foam had completely enveloped the little car.

Simultaneously, three firemen went forward into the knee-deep foam to force open the car door with a power tool and then gently eased its unconcious driver out. They carefully carried him over towards me and then laid him down, after which the casualty suddenly jumped up, brushed the foam off his fire tunic, stood to attention and saluted me.

'Welcome to Biggleswade and Old Warden, sir! I'm Station Officer Newman. Bernard Newman,' and held out his hand. 'I believe in creating realistic training and this is typical of what we get up to.'

I must have given him a slightly puzzled look because he went on:

'The Mini is supposed to be a light aircraft in trouble and I use it like this now and again.'

When I enquired about the ownership of the Mini he said 'Well, it's mine actually and I only use it locally. It's a pretty reliable old bus.'

By now the crews had washed most of the foam and dry powder off the Mini, but it still looked a real mess. I noticed that one of its front windows was partially open. There were pools of water on the car floor and the seats looked distinctly soggy.

Now the postscript to this unusual training enterprise was that during an air rally at Old Warden the following summer, a light aircraft collided with another on the runway whilst landing and caught fire. One of the pilots was killed and there were a number of other casualties although these were minimised thanks to some prompt action by onlookers and the speedy work of the Biggleswade crew.

I also responded to this crash as the duty senior officer but with a journey of some ten miles to negotiate as well as the air show crowds nearer to Old Warden, the emergency was all over by the time I arrived. Station Officer Newman came over to brief me on the accident situation, and then took me over to the white foam covered wreckage on the grass runway about a hundred yards away.

'It could have been far, far worse,' he said rather quietly.

I looked over towards the thousand or so spectators who were milling around the display and exhibition areas close by, and nodded in agreement.

As we walked towards the still steaming pile of torn and twisted metal, Bigglewade firefighters were beginning to roll up the hose lines which snaked back across the grass to their two fire engines. A light wind was blowing small flecks of foam up into the breeze like the start of a snowstorm.

And as I left the scene shortly afterwards, it occured to me that for a little while at least, Bernard Newman's old blue Mini might just be going to enjoy a well earned rest.

11
A Better Day Tomorrow?

When I first joined the fire service back in 1963, firemen in Great Britain answered about 350,000 fire and accident emergency calls per year. Sadly, around 770 men, women and children perished in fires, and some 5,000 received serious life threatening injuries. The measurable fire loss was approximately £275 million, literally all going up in smoke.

Now nearly three decades on, UK firefighters answer around a staggering one million '999' calls per year. Despite an enormous effort by fire brigades and other associated bodies in the field of fire safety education, the annual UK loss of life in fires remains at about 750 to 800, and most of these fatalities and serious fire injuries now occur in the home.

A string of UK fire tragedies over the last fifty years brought in its wake new fire safety 'stable door' legislation, specific to certain types of premises. This has certainly seen a great reduction in the number of fatal fires in commercial and industrial buildings.

Thus those who lost their lives in Bristol (Petrol station, 1951, 22 dead); Keighley, West Riding of Yorkshire (Mill, 1956, 8 dead); Liverpool (Department Store, 1960, 11 dead); Bolton, Lancashire (Club, 1961, 19 dead); Saffron Walden, Essex (Hotel, 1969, 11 dead) and Bradford (Football Stadium, 1985, 56 dead), may not have died in vain.

The most alarming modern day statistic is that of the annual UK fire loss, which has now gone up fourfold since 1963 and has exceeded £1 billion per year for the first time. Unfortunately, fires caused by arson are also on the increase, as are the number of malicious '999' calls which turn out firefighters to hoax incidents, a practice which can deprive an area of proper fire cover.

The principal causes of fire still remain much the same as when I joined the service. Misuse of electrical equipment, cooking left unattended, smokers carelessly disposing of their cigarette ends, and children playing with matches all continue to cause their toll of human suffering and material fire damage. For fires don't just happen, they are caused.

And the toxic and pernicious nature of smoke produced from even a small quantity of modern plastic can cause death much faster than the products of smoke from fires of relatively few years ago. For it is a fallacy to imagine that fire fatalities are caused by people being 'burnt' to death. In almost every modern fire death men, women and children are asphyxiated by thick choking smoke, long before their bodies are consumed by flames.

This has also meant a much wider increase in the use of breathing apparatus by firefighters. In my earlier days only every other fire engine carried breathing sets, and even then, these were only reluctantly called into use when smoke levels inside a burning building had become impossible. Nowadays, the smoke from even a *small* fire can be so acrid and unbreathable that firefighters in the street *outside* a fire affected building require respiratory protection.

And the job goes on being more dangerous. In 1990, six firemen were killed in action at separate incidents whilst about 900 firefighters were seriously injured. As if this level of danger is not enough, recent urban disturbances in various cities and towns have seen fire crews and their fire engines being on the receiving end of bricks and bottles. In one recent such incident in Manchester, a fire engine alloy ladder actually sustained sniper gunfire damage!

But there are the positive sides to all this. About half of Britain's homes are now fitted with simple yet effective smoke alarms, whilst firefighters are probably better equipped and trained then ever before. Nevertheless, given the technical complexities of modern firefighting, allied to the 24 hour nature and demands of the profession in all weathers, perhaps today's young men and women recruits need to have a handful of science degrees as well as the strength and endurance of a navvy, and be a jack of all trades into the bargain.

Naturally, after such an eventful career I find myself remembering certain fires and other emergencies more than others. One such turnout was to my first large London fire, in the Grocers Livery Hall, in the heart of City of London. 50 pumps were needed on this job and the devastation of such a fine and ornate structure was breathtaking to behold. At one stage during firefighting operations, a huge chandelier crashed down just in front of where my crew were working in fairly thick smoke at the bottom of a staircase. As the glass fragments showered over all of us like sharp confetti, how glad I was as an inexperienced fireman to feel the reassuring and calming hand of our Sub Officer on my shoulder.

Other major London fires can be remembered for different reasons. At a large West Kensington sports goods warehouse, I was one of 150 firefighters who witnessed a most spectacular and explosive flashover. Its fiery force blew an entire end wall out into the street below, damaging several fire engines but causing only minor injuries amongst the fire crews.

Another major conflagration, remembered for its particular smell, was a 30 pump job in a disused Victorian cold store in Battle Bridge Lane just off Tooley Street, close by the River Thames at London Bridge. The entire six floor building was lined with cork in order to provide insulation, and years of the storage of fats and other flammable produce made the entire structure a tinder box. At the height of the fire, flames were lighting up the entire area as if it were floodlit. To this day, I cannot ever recall fighting such an intensely fierce and stubborn fire, nor one where there was such a pungent aroma all around the adjoining riverside streets. The smoke from all that burning cork was pretty awful too! The London Brigade were in attendance for two full weeks before the last deep seated glowing embers were out, and the district resumed some normality.

A smaller London fire in Stoke Newington posed rather different problems. It occurred in a turkish delight manufacturers where there were hundreds of sacks of sugar stored in the warehouse involved in the outbreak. The sprinkler system had actuated early on and assisted the containment of the fire, but had dissolved much of the stored sugar into a huge sticky mess. This had slowly run everywhere and our hoses, lighting and other equipment as well as each uniform became covered in the glue-like treacle. We literally spent hours back at the fire station, scraping and cleaning the awful stuff off, and even now I am unable to face turkish delight without recalling the aroma of all that burning sugar.

Another major London fire is worth recalling if only to remember a particular senior officer who taught me much of my firemanship and command techniques. The outbreak was during 1975 and started in the complex known as Grand Buildings, Northumberland Avenue, a seven floor office block which turned out to be a rabbit warren of corridors and interconnecting passageways. Grand Buildings overlooked Trafalgar Square and, of course, Nelson's Column.

Smoke from the growing flames in the basement was first noticed at about dawn, around 0500 hours. By the time the first London Fire Brigade fire engines arrived, a very serious fire was spiralling maliciously up a lift shaft and beginning to break out through the roof, consuming all in its ferocious path. Within some thirty minutes, about 100 firemen with twenty fire engines from fire stations all over central London were at work.

At about 0530 hours, the duty senior fire officer – the Divisional Commander of the West End area – arrived to take charge. He was a much loved, no nonsense officer, known to his firefighter crews as 'Nick'.

Nick got out of his staff car and pulled on his battle

scarred white fire helmet to complete his firefighting uniform. With hands on hips, he quickly surveyed the frontage of the smoking building with experienced eyes and then purposefully strode towards the incident control unit parked close to the foot of Nelson's Column.

'If we don't get moving' he shouted, 'we are going to lose this whole bloody corner of Trafalgar Square!'

Even those crews working some distance away could hear that Nick had arrived. Indeed, his high decibel level and voice projection, each well developed after many years of the noise and danger of the fireground, were Nick's hallmarks, as well as always leading from the front.

The officer in charge of the Control Unit looked somewhat harrassed. Setting up control of a major fire was always hectic in the first half hour or so.

'Come on, man!' repeated the veteran as he drew breath in deeply, before going on to issue his next command.

'I want six more breathing apparatus crews here on the double. And get a f------ move on!'

With this stentorian stream, most of the remaining pigeons took off to seek refuge on rooftops opposite. It was enough to wake Nelson on the top of his Column some 175 feet above the square. If he had been able to look down at the toiling firefighters below, he might just have recalled that for most of the 19th century, London firemen had almost exclusively been recruited from the ranks of Royal Navy matelots. Years of long duty systems, harsh discipline and danger, as well as being strong and able to work at heights, made them ideal firefighters.

By 0800 hours, the fire was surrounded and coming under control. But with Trafalgar Square closed off to traffic and the crowds held back, many firemen in breathing apparatus were still struggling with heavy hoses on the smoke filled hot floors and staircases inside Grand Buildings.

Nick was by then engaged on a reconnaissance accompanied by several officers. As he was negotiating a narrow fire weakened staircase on the upper floors, a door suddenly fell across his path and landed heavily on his right foot.

Protesting violently that he was alright, Nick was half carried and helped down to street level and out to fresh air, where he was put in the back of a waiting ambulance. There, despite some loud profanities, his fire boot was eased off to reveal some bleeding and badly bruised toes. Nick swore even louder whilst the ambulance crew tended his injury.

Above the smoke haze below, Nelson might have blinked into life once again and reflected for the second time that morning, that the noise of warriors under fire in modern battle sounded much the same as they had done at the Nile, Cadiz and Trafalgar all those years ago.

One other London memory concerns a small, yet fatal, nightime fire in a solitary dwelling above a delicatessen shop in Frith Street, Soho. A two man breathing apparatus crew had used high pressure hosereels to knock a serious fire down at the top of the second floor stairs, and after a brief search amid the heat and smoke, came upon the body of the female flat tenant, still reclining in a charred armchair.

She turned out to be 84 years of age, and something of a recluse who in recent years had rarely left her little flat in the heart of Soho. All around the fire and smoke damaged home, were her personal possessions and many of these were of Victorian and Edwardian origin. The kitchen and its equipment was like being in a time warp. Once the fire was completely out, the flat was left untouched awaiting the arrival of the fire investigation forensic team. It appeared that the octogenarian had some-how set fire to herself in the armchair, but further specialist forensic work was needed to verify this.

As the firefighters cleared up and restowed all the hosereels and other gear back onto the three fire engines down in street below, I looked through the charred window opening and out across the Soho rooftops at the rising sun. All around were the sounds of London and its people coming to life at the start of another day. I turned to look at the blackened lifeless body of the old lady, whose upper torso and clothes were quite badly burned, and quietly said a prayer in the hope that her end had been painless and swift.

Some memorable incidents after my promotion from London to several shire county fire brigades are also worth mentioning. In Bedfordshire, the summer always brought weeks of activity during the cereal crop stubble burning season. A number of stubble fires got out of control, and on one occasion driven by the wind, threatened a entire village in the path of the fire. Sparks or flying brands from the stubble fire had also got into an adjacent crop of standing barley and the speed with which the wall of fire came down the hillside towards village properties was frightening.

Only by creating a hundred yard long curtain of powerful water spray were we able to keep the intense fire from consuming a number of bungalows and houses right in the path of the flames. As it was, one fire crew had to abandon their fire engine in a field nearby when the wind veered and suddenly pushed the last vestiges of the original fire under its wheels. All this effort in full fire kit was during an afternoon when the temperature soared to 28 degrees Centigrade, and there was a real risk of dehydration amongst the firefighters present before they were able to be spared to take welcome liquid refreshment at the mobile canteen unit.

Weather conditions are rarely on the side of fire crews, and so it was at one particular wintertime fire whilst I served in South Wales. A serious fire had broken out during the early morning in a large hotel at Merthyr Tydfil.

After a very hazardous drive to the fire on roads made treacherous by black ice, I saw a rare sight. The fire hydrant pits were full of frozen snow and ice, and petrol was being poured into several of these pits and then ignited to enable fire hoses to be connected.

The sight of several blazing sections of pavement at either end of a burning building is a very strange sight, but without such drastic steps, the onboard fire engine water supplies would have quickly been used up. The next morning the Meteriological Office confirmed that the temperature had dived as low as − 14 degrees C, and having slipped and shivered around the hotel fire all night long, I well believed the weather men.

Memories of my years in West Sussex recall some of the sweat and toil involved in fighting fires in thatched properties. It is quite incredible just how much reed goes into a thatched roof. When a fire breaks out the best tactics are to cut a firebreak right through the thatch as quickly as possible, in order to isolate the flames and try to prevent the fire spreading into the structure proper.

To rapidly cut into a burning thatched roof demands both plenty of working hands and several ladders carefully pitched onto the roof itself. Many thatch properties tend, of course, to be in rural locations where the nearest fire station is some travel time away, and water supplies may be less than satisfactory. Hence, I have seen some dour struggles as retained fire crews have worked valiantly to open up a cottage roof where tiny orange flames have kept stubbornly appearing through the thatch.

Success at a thatch fire also means that firefighters have to ensure that as the burning thatch is damped and removed from the roof to ground level, it must be spread out well clear of the building concerned. On one occasion, I saw smouldering thatch piled so high all around a house at Handcross where half the roof had been saved, that it looked like we had added a thatched outer wall ten feet tall! Like stubble fires, the sweat and toil involved in dealing with thatch fires really has to be experienced to be believed, and any city firefighter who thinks thatch fires are an easy touch should think again.

Towards the end of my uniformed career I was unexpectedly able to be part of a simple, yet moving, act of remembrance following the death of a firefighter. It took place in November 1990 at the Fire Service College at Moreton-in-Marsh in Gloucestershire, where I had been lecturing during the morning to a course of senior fire officers from a number of brigades.

The Fire Service College is the central fire training establishment of the UK, and probably the world, for such is its pre-eminence that it has progressively drawn fire service students from all continents. For the College facilities at Moreton embrace not only command, leadership and management teaching, but also the sciences and fire service law, and a wide range of associated developmental subjects.

Outside of the lecture rooms are a quite amazing range of 'hot fire' buildings in and around which young fire officers can build upon their skills amid the hostile environment of their profession. The College also has its own section of motorway and railway line, a 4,000 ton ship, as well as chemical rigs and oil and gas tanks. At any one time in the academic year, there will be around 500 students of all ranks present.

So it was on this November morning when, my morning session over, I joined the staff and students at lunch in the large dining hall. But before lunch could commence, there was a brief but very special ceremony to be enacted. Located on the wall at the far end of the dining hall is a polished brass bell which is rung on the announcement of a death of a firefighter, to sound a one minute silence immediately before lunch is taken.

The previous day, a Leading Firefighter in the Cornwall County Fire Brigade based at Newquay fire station had been taking part in a Turntable Ladder training drill when the upper section of the extended ladder had collapsed. He had been at the ladder top, and fallen to his death.

Although this ceremony at the College was fairly recently instituted, the list of firefighters who had since lost their lives and been commemorated by the solemn ringing of the bell and having their names inscribed on the adjacent brass roll of honour, was already a long one.

And despite being a regular visitor to the College over many years, both as a student and latterly as a speaker, this was the first time I participated in the 'bell' ceremony.

As all the lunchtime diners stood quietly behind their chairs, the assembly was called to order and silence descended. A brief statement that Leading Firefighter Stephen Taylor of the Cornwall Brigade had met his death whilst taking part in a training exercise was read out. Then the youngest student of the brigade involved attending the College at that time, stepped forward and rang the bell three times. A one minute silence followed, during which the 500 strong assembly of uniformed men and women from fire brigades of Great Britain and around the world, paid silent homage to the Cornish firefighter.

My reflections have to conclude with two very different major fires which took place during my service in Devon. The first of these was the conflagration which destroyed the upper floors of the Dingles department store in Plymouth city centre, just before midnight on the night of 19 December 1988.

The fire, believed to have been caused by arsonists, was well advanced by the time that the first city fire crews arrived, only some three minutes after the first of many '999' calls. Assistance was quickly called for and as the fire escalated, my telephone rang to tell me that ten pumps were now at the scene.

I dressed quickly and was soon driving fast down the M5 and then onto the A38 towards Sir Frances Drake's fair city. It was a beautifully clear night, and as I finally topped the A38 hill at Marsh Mills, Plymouth lay spread out below. Dramatically visible even at that distance of some five miles, and despite the glare of the distant city street lighting, was a huge red angry fireball and a black smoke pall which rose high into the starry sky.

The Dingle's fire took over four hours to control during which eighteen pumps and four Turntable Ladders were used. At one stage there was a flashover across the second floor of the store whilst breathing apparatus crews were working inside close by. Fortunately, there were no injuries although several fire engines, including a new Dennis, and two ladders were damaged by falling masonry. At one stage the fire threatened to spread out into other department stores nearby. Fortunately, the fire was eventually confined within the Dingles complex but even so, the fire loss was initially put at £22 million.

For many older citizens of Plymouth the scene as dawn broke the morning after, with smoke and steam still pouring out of Dingle's, was reminiscent of the Luftwaffe raids on the city during 1942. Like those earlier times of drama, this was also a night to remember.

Then on the night of 4 September 1990, fire engulfed the town centre of Totnes, in South Devon. Totnes is one of the best examples of preserved Elizabethan architecture with its narrow courtyards and closely packed historic buildings around the hilltop town centre.

On this windy night, the fire quickly took hold as it spread from one historic premises to another, then jumped across the narrow streets to other buildings. At one stage, fourteen separate ancient premises were involved as 120 firefighters used ladders to mount a concerted rooftop water attack to surround the fire and restrict the damage. Fortunately no lives were lost, although there were several lucky escapes by residents during the evacuation of parts of the town centre.

As with the Dingle's fire, I was told of escalating seriousness of the Totnes outbreak by Fire Control just as I was preparing to go to bed, and quickly got into my car and booked mobile on the radio which was busy with the responses of the many fire crews now rushing to the aid of the Totnes firefighters. There was little traffic about at around midnight, and switching my headlights and blue beacon on, I swung the car out of the drive and set off for Totnes.

And as at so many nightime turnouts over the years, both on fire engines and later in fire cars, the intense blue shaft of light from the rotating beacon on my car roof bounced off the darkness of the night all around. I wondered what drama would face me upon my arrival at the fire, and felt that old and familiar excitement ripple through me yet again.

Further Reading

Blackstone, G. V. *A History of the British Fire Service* (Routledge & Kegan Paul, 1957).

Fire & Water – The London Firefighter's Blitz 1940–42 Remembered (Lindsay Drummond, 1942; New Edition, Firestorm Publications, 1992).

Fire Directory (The Yellow Book) 1992/93 (FMJ International Publications).

Fire Protection Association – various fire safety publications.

HMSO Annual Reports of Her Majesty's Chief Inspectors of Fire Services for England and Wales, and Scotland.

Holloway, Sally. *London's Noble Fire Brigades* (Cassell, 1973)

Holloway, Sally. *Moorgate* (David & Charles, 1988)

Honeycombe, Gordon. *Red Watch* (Hutchinson, 1976; Arrow 1977)

Jackson, W. Eric. *London's Fire Brigades* (Longmans, 1966)

Nicholls, Arthur. *Going to Blazes* (Hale, 1978)

Wallington, Neil. *Fireman! A Personal Account* (David & Charles, 1979)

Wallington, Neil. *Firemen at War* (David & Charles, 1982)

Wallington, Neil. *'999' – The Accident and Crash Rescue Work of the Fire Service* (David & Charles, 1987)

Wallington, Neil. *Images of Fire* (David & Charles, 1989)

Ranks in the British Fire Service

Fireman/Firefighter	crew member of appliance
Leading Fireman/Firefighter	In charge of appliance
Sub Officer	In charge of watch (shift) and appliance
Station Officer	In charge of station
Assistant Divisional Officer	In charge of larger station/several stations
Divisional Officer	In charge of group of stations (a division)
Senior Divisional Officer	In charge of large division
Assistant Chief Officer	Based at headquarters and responsible for wide range of support activities. Also takes command at large incidents
Deputy Chief Fire Officer	As for ACO but deputises for CFO
Chief Fire Officer	In command of brigade and responsible to the fire authority

Fireman

by Charles Clisby

Reporter asked me: 'What's it like?'

I shrugged him off: 'I couldn't say.'
You see, I'm not a one for that,
Not one for bragging anyway.

He pressed me hard – and so I tried;
I hoped my tale he understood.
Could it be that telling him
Might do the job a bit of good?

'If you put on six overcoats –
And though you suffered hell from corns
You crammed your feet in army boots –
Wore on your head a crown of thorns –
Lay in a bath, first hot, then cold –
Got out and ran a mile or so –
Into an oven squeezed yourself
And turned to nine the regulo;
If, with a bandage round your eyes;
A wooden peg clipped on your nose,
You then crawled through a concrete maze;
Your feet wrapped round with yards of hose –
You'd get a notion what it's like.'

Reporter laughed: 'It can't be true.'

I looked him in the eyes and said:
'You're right. Five overcoats will do.'